The Psychic Soldier Seri

The Psychic Soldier Series-Book 2-A Soldier is Born

Welcome to this series about the Psychic Soldier and his exciting adventures growing up in the nineteenth century.

In Book 2 he learns to fight as a solider and acquires real psychic abilities to help him.

These abilities are real and the Author has written about a realistic process for their development since he is worldwide authority on Eastern Spiritual development and Psychic abilities. See his nonfiction books such as "God Like Powers & Abilities." to learn more.

In this first episode we learn about Tristan Morgan's early life and adventures with partially developed intuitive abilities.

He also meets masters of ancient wisdom and technology to learn from them.

Tristan Morgan also learns how to live many lifetimes so future adventures will focus dates fifty or one hundred years into his future.

The story is fictional, but it could be real. This is not pure fantasy.

Find out how amazing real life could really be.

The Psychic Soldier Series-Book 2-A Soldier is Born

The Psychic Soldier Series-Book 2-A Soldier is Born

Copyright Page

The Psychic Soldier Series–Book 2-A Soldier is Born

The Psychic Soldier Series-Book 2-A Soldier is Born

The Psychic Soldier Series-Book 2-A Soldier is Born

Other books by Martin K. Ettington

Spiritual and Metaphysics Books:
Prophecy: A History and How to
    Guide
God Like Powers and Abilities
Enlightenment for Newbies
Removing Illusions to Find True
    Happiness
Using the Scientific Method to
    Study the Paranormal
A Compendium of Metaphysics
    and How to Guides (Six books
    together in one volume)
Love From the Heart
The Enlightenment Experience
Learn Your Soul's Purpose
Pursuing Enlightenment
A Modern Man's Search for Truth

Longevity & Immortality:
Physical Immortality: A History and
    How to Guide
The Commentaries of Living
    Immortals
Records of Extremely Long Lived
    Persons
Enlightenment and Immortality
Longevity Improvements from
    Science
The 10 Principles of Personal
    Longevity
Personal Freedom & Longevity
Telomeres & Longevity
The Diets and Lifestyles of the
    Worlds Oldest Peoples
The Longevity Six Books Bundle

Science Fiction:
Out of This Universe
Personal Freedom-Parts 1 & 2
The Psychic Soldier Series:
    Book 1-Himalayan Journey
    Book 2-A Soldier is Born
    Book 3-Fighting For Right
    Book 4-Earth Protector
    Book 5-War on the Astral Plane
The Immortality Sci Fi Bundle

The God Like Powers Series:
Human Invisibility

Invulnerability and Shielding
Teleportation
Psychokinesis
Our Energy Body, Auras, and
    Thoughtforms
The God Like Powers Series—
    Volume 1 Compilation

The Yoga Discovery Series:
Yoga-An Ancient Art Form
Hatha Yoga-Helping you Live
    Better
Raja Yoga-Through the Ages
The Yoga Discovery Package

Business Books:
Creating, Publishing, & Marketing
    Practitioner Ebooks
Building a Successful Longevity
    Coaching Business
Why Become a Coach?
The Professional Coaching
    Success Trilogy

Science and Technology
Aliens and Secret Technology
Designing and Building Space
    Colonies
Future Predictions By and
    Engineer & Seer
The Unusual Science &
    Technology Bundle
The Real Atlantis-In the Eye of the
    Sahara

The Psychic Soldier Series-Book 2-A Soldier is Born

<u>The Longevity Training Series</u>

(A transcription of the online Multimedia Longevity Coaching Training Program)

The Personal Longevity Training Series-Book1-Long Lived Persons
The Personal Longevity Training Series-Book2-Your Soul's Purpose
The Personal Longevity Training Series-Book3-Enable Your Life Urge
The Personal Longevity Training Series-Book4-Your Spiritual Connection
The Personal Longevity Training Series-Book5-Having Love in Your Heart
The Personal Longevity Training Series-Book6-Energy Body Health
The Personal Longevity Training Series-Book7-The Science of Longevity
The Personal Longevity Training Series-Book8-Physical Body Health
The Personal Longevity Training Series-Book9-Avoiding Accidents
The Personal Longevity Training Series-Book10-Implementing These Principles

The Personal Longevity Training Series-Books One Thru Ten

These books are all available in digital and printed formats from my website and on Amazon, Barnes & Noble, and Apple ITunes
Website: http://mkettingtonbooks.com Audiobooks available on Amazon, Audible.com, and ITunes. Website: http://mkettingtonbooks.co

The Psychic Soldier Series-Book 2-A Soldier is Born

Table of Contents

My Early Life...1

Regimental Operations 13

On My Own 19

Matana's Story 25

Into the Mountains.. 29

The Trip to Tibet... 35

Struggling to Live 37

The School of the Gods 41

Going to School.. 47

Year Two in School 55

Traveling Further East....................................... 65

The Chinese Warlord 69

Travel Across the Orient 77

Prisoner.. 85

In the Royal Court 89

Longevity 95

In Japan.. 103

The Christian Mission....................................... 109

Visiting America.. 121

The Gold Rush 127

Volcano Town Sherriff....................................... 141

Indian Country 149

The Comanches.. 155

The Psychic Soldier Series-Book 2-A Soldier is Born

Meeting the Hopis 167

The Grand Canyon... 173

The City of Arakesh... 179

Back To School 187

Back with the Hopis... 192

The Psychic Soldier Series-Book 2-A Soldier is Born

Cast of Characters

The Psychic Warrior:	Tristan Morgan Tristan's Sisters Sarah, Jana, Rache and Kathy
Lieutenant in London	Lt. Ford
Regimental Commander	Colonel Briggs
My platoon Commander	Lieutenant Milborn
Healer in Small town northern India	Matana Virk
Wise man in Nepal village	Mr. Nasim
Head of the School of the Gods	Lama Gingding
Spiritual Instructor in School	Mr. Tsao
Girlfriend in school	Raina
Family on Silk Road	Tasir Malmade
Chinese Emperors Spiritual Advisor	Minister Valdasian
Christian Mission in Japan	Briana
Attacking Gang Leader	Ramanda
Evil Miner in Sierras	Sam Twist
Friend in Volcano town	Wanda
Criminal in Volcano town	Terry the Hatchet
Hopi Indian in Santa Fe	Cochito
Hopi Indian Maiden	Chepi
Elder in Arakesh	Melitor

The Psychic Soldier Series-Book 2-A Soldier is Born

Guide in Arakesh	Tilvi
Head Master in Arakesh	Master Levindo
Teacher in Arakesh	Master Kalabra

My Early Life

My name is Tristin Morgan and this is the story of my life—and long one at that.

I decided to break my autobiography into multiple phases since I've now lived over two thousand years and it would take way too long to tell everything in one book.

I was born in 1828 in Wales west of England near the city of Cardiff to a farming family out in the countryside.

I never had plans to become a warrior, and fate intervened in ways I never would have expected.

My early life was pretty typical of living on a farm where we grew crops and tended sheep.

I learned to do chores from the age of five years old. These chores included feeding the sheep and helping my Dad with the wheat and barley crops.

Spent many a day helping with weed pulling or putting down fertilizer and rescuing sheep from gullies or those caught in fences.

At ten years old I was five feet tall—pretty big for my age. I was thin and wiry and would only become more so as I grew into a gangly teenager.

My four sisters were great fun since I was the middle child—two older and two younger. They all wanted to play with me.

My sister's names were Sarah, Jana, Rachel, and Kathy.

I learned I was different one day from this adventure when I was eight years old:

The Psychic Soldier Series-Book 2-A Soldier is Born

It was midafternoon and I was done with chores. Went was out with my bow and arrow in the local woods shooting squirrels.

Had been doing lots of shooting and missing the squirrels. My dad told me it was good practice but it would take me a while to become a good hunter. It didn't happen overnight.

Spotted a big grey one who saw me and took off for his tree.

He ran up the tree which was about twenty feet from me. I had a feeling he would jump left onto a branch rather than right to an adjacent close tree.

So I aimed left—sure enough, I hit the squirrel!

He fell out of the tree and I ran home with it in my hands to show my parents.

My dad was excited for me and gave me a big smile and said "I knew you could become a real hunter if you stuck with it!"

Mom told me good work and started skinning the squirrel to put into her stew pot.

It tasted great with dinner as food you got yourself always does.

Continue my hunting for the next several years and became a real "dead eye" shot.

My parents and friends from neighboring farms came with me to watch me shoot because I rarely missed.

What they didn't realize was that I was using my intuition to judge where the prey would go and so it was pretty easy for me.

All the people watching just assume I had great "woodsman" skills and that I was watching the animals closely.

The Psychic Soldier Series-Book 2-A Soldier is Born

I had little formal schooling but did learn to read and write since my mother taught me.

All too soon my life on the farm seemed too close and contained for me.

Really wanted to get away and do something with my life.

Some of my older friends had travelled to London and many soldiers came back to the area to visit their families.

These soldiers told many stories of travels to distant lands like India and Australia.

I was now sixteen and antsy to get out and see the world.

Told my parents I was going to join the army to see the world. Both of them stared at me but knew they weren't going to change my mind.

They were sad to see me leave and made me promise I would come back and see them.

My dad even had wet eyes as he gave me some shillings for food and rides to London.

My sisters all hugged me goodbye and I could see tears in their eyes.

Waving to my family in the front of the house was tough and I nearly changed my mind, but I was set to go and so I set off with some clothes on my back, a small pack with extras, and a knife on my belt.

I knew how to use the knife to skin animals and had played fighting with my friends, but wasn't a very good knife fighter.

*****

The Psychic Soldier Series-Book 2-A Soldier is Born

My first night on the road I walked towards Cardiff and stayed on the side of the road in a dry haystack.

The next day I made it to Cardiff. After several inquiries I found some food carts going to London.

The owner of one cart let me ride for free if I was willing to load and unload the cart.

It was more work than I thought because the owner Ralph stopped in nearly every town on the way to sell part of his load and load some new freight on his large wagon.

It took us about five days to get to London. I thanked Ralph for the ride and he suggested a local low cost tavern that had safe and low cost rooms for the night.

I got to the tavern and decided to order some beer with my dinner food. It was an old establishment with some seedy people in it.

Ordering a second and third beer was a mistake. Feeling pretty good and not used to being drunk I wandered outside into a dark alley nearby to take a leak.

There were several scrawny but mean looking toughs in the alley who saw me and quickly surrounded me.

They told me to give them my money, but drunk as I was I told them to "go eat shit".

This led to two on them pulling out knifes and telling me they were going to spear me like a pig.

I pulled my knife and now I was scared. This caused me to sober up quickly and really focus my attention on my muggers.

One started to lean in to strike me. My intuition was to pirouette and stab him in his arm. Then felt that another one was going to stab me in the back.

This led me to reach backwards turning left and put a big gash into the second attacker's chest.

They quickly decided I wasn't an easy mark and ran out the end of the alley.

I was left there sweating and breathing hard.

A soldier who I could tell was a full Lieutenant came into the alley and remarked "I was going to ask if you were okay or need help, but I see you can defend yourself."

He clapped me on the back and said "My name is Lieutenant Ford and let me stand you to a drink"

I said thanks as Lt. Ford let me back inside. He was almost six feet tall and looked like he was well bred and in his mid-twenties.

We sat down and I could see the Lieutenant was much more experienced in the world than myself.

I asked him "How come you are an officer and at a young age?" He told me "My dad purchased my commission. I've been in the Infantry for about a year and we are going to deploy in a few months"

"Where are you going?" He replied "To India, There is lots of action there and it will be a great adventure."

I asked him "How can I join the army and go with you?" He gave me a sharp look then nodded his head.

"I'll take you to the recruiting office tomorrow. You sure you want to do this? It can be a hard life."

The Psychic Soldier Series-Book 2-A Soldier is Born

I said "Yes" and we agreed to meet in the morning.

He took me to an old building built of brick in London which had a short line of recruits.

An old Sergeant inside asked me questions about how I was raised and didn't really listen to the answers. I think he just wanted to see if I could hold a conversation properly.

Then he gave me a paper to make my mark or sign up. Joining was easy since they needed recruits.

I was sent with a group of other kids to the Regiment's training barracks North of London.

Over several months we learned to dig trenches, fire muskets, and it included lots of marching.

Discipline was tough. I remember being called to order one Sunday morning to watch two soldiers who got drunk the night before be flogged.

They each got twenty lashes and had to be helped down from the flogging stand to get salve put on their wounds in the barracks.

I determined to not do anything to get flogged since it looked very painful.

After a few months I was considered fully trained. The non comms told us all I would become more fully trained in battle.

Word got around we were going overseas. We were assembled one morning on the parade ground.

The Major who was second in charge of the regiment got up on a platform to speak to us.

He said "You are now all fully trained soldiers in the glorious British Army. Now we are going on an exciting deployment to India. I expect you all to make your leaders and the British Empire proud."

*****

The next morning we rode carts to the London Harbor to join our troop ship for the journey to India.

I saw Lieutenant Ford on the ship with other officers. Waving at him to get his attention he finally saw me.

He headed towards me and I met him and saluted him.

He smiled and said "Private Morgan I see you are making the trip with us." I replied "Yes Sir. I made it through training and am coming to India with you"

He looked at me seriously and advised me "Be careful Private. There are many in the army who pick on others and some who are pure sadists. Learn who to avoid and who to be careful with if you value your life".

"Thanks Sir. I will be careful"

Traveling to India

The ship headed down through the Mediterranean and on to Cairo.

We were only called to do light exercise on trip and most of the day was free so I spent a lot of time at the guard rails or looking through open windows.

I really enjoyed seeing the Rock of Gibraltar and knowing it was a British Fort.

It was July and a lot hotter than anywhere in England. Passing Gibraltar I was impressed with the large canons and could see how it stood as a barrier to hostile forces entering or leaving the Mediterranean.

We reached Cairo after several weeks in our sailing ship and debarked to a British Barracks in the City.

Out that evening with some of my mates we wandered into downtown Cairo to find a bar.

We got liquored up and headed down some streets to look around.

I soon felt the hair rising on my neck and told my mates—let's not go down this alley.

It feels pretty dangerous. Most listened, but several didn't care and wandered down there.

We soon heard yelling and we converged on the alley along with a few British Marines in the area.

One of my squad's solders had been stabbed pretty badly and robbed by the locals. They were still attacking him. I ran in a started hitting them and stabbed at a couple with my knife. They could see my mates coming too so they took off running.

We carried him back to the barracks and a corpsman was called to work on him.

Fortunately the solder survived but he would be in bed for weeks and would miss the rest of our regiment's trip to India.

The Regimental commander lined all of us up who had been at the incident to get our stories.

The commander was in his forties and had a big handlebar mustache. His name was Colonel Briggs and he had a deep voice.

He got the overall story about the incident and my warning to the rest.

He looked me up and down then said "Private Morgan here seems to keep his head about him. You should all listen to what he says"

The rest of my mates stared at me but didn't say anything.

Then he dismissed us and we got an early rest that night.

Next morning we all joined a caravan to take us to the Red Sea Port of Suez. This was where we would catch our next ship.

We had camels and horses pulling wagons with troops and supplies in the wagons.

We did a lot of walking but sometimes got to ride in the wagons under the canvas shaded canopies.

Several officers remarked that there were ideas about building a canal to the Red Sea but it might be decades before a serious effort was made.

It was hot as hell in the desert and we stayed under the tarps on the wagons as much as possible.

It took five days to get to the port city of Suez and were happy to see the water.

After we were all dismissed most of us headed to the beach to jump into the water. God but that water felt nice and cool…

*****

The next morning we boarded a ship owned by the British East India Company. It was this company which really controlled all of India and had a warrant from the British Crown to do so.

Our regiment would really be contracting with British East India Company while in India.

The company also had a huge army of natives of over one hundred thousand in India.

Our ship hugged the coast and we reached India in another two weeks and exited the ship in Bombay.

A crowded city even then with people everywhere and all of the colors of the rainbow in what people wore for clothes and the local street shops.

Although we spent a few weeks in the Bombay area it wasn't our final destination.

Our ultimate destination was Bengal state in northeastern India, so it was back onto several East India Company boats to travel around the south of India to the city of Calcutta.

The Psychic Soldier Series-Book 2-A Soldier is Born

The sea was crowded with small fishing boats near the cities, and the weather was steaming. If not for the water we were on we would have dried up.

We finally got to the east coast of India with lots of sailing and stops in small ports on the way for supplies.

I was on supply duty sometimes and would be in the row boats heading into the city.

Each city was different and had many beggars. Some large stone shrines to the many Indian Gods existed in some of those cities.

We got provisions, water, and some fresh fruit to forestall any possibilities of scurvy.

As we came down the ramp into Calcutta we could see that it was a much more crowded city and much poorer than Bombay.

We got a couple days rest in an army camp, then two weeks more marching through the dust north into central Bengal.

I was convinced I'd become a desert warrior from all of the dust and dirt which we walked through. This included a continuous cloud of dust raised by our horses and the soldiers in front of us.

We all wore handkerchiefs which we moistened often to catch the dust.

We climbed he trails for another week until we got into the rainy forests to reach our destination.

Finally we reached a Raja's Palace in central Bengal and were told this was going to be our Regimental quarters.

Regimental Operations

The former owner of the palace was the Nawab Nizam of Bengal. His army was defeated by the British in the late seventeen hundreds.

Now the palace was to be the home of our regiment and two more in this province were nearby.

The location was several thousand feet up in the hills so the climate was cooler, and we had rivers and streams in the area.

Overall, it was a nice temperate location. There was lots of grass and trees, with cool mountain mists in the morning.

We were warned to watch for tigers in the local woods and wealthy visitors plus our commanders often went into the bush on elephants to hunt the tigers.

Our barracks were a series of buildings added onto to back of the palace in the last few decades. Overall, not too bad.

We had plenty of training time to learn better shooting and close quarter combat practice with our rifle bayonets.

I spent my off time around the outdoor fire next to our quarters.

We spent many an evening shooting the breeze with each other while listening to wild animal noises in the woods.

My mate Rossiter leaned back on a log near the fire and said "This is the life. I could stay here like this for many years."

However, old Sergeant Woods who was sitting around the fire said "Wrong laddie, I don't think you properly understand the situation. We aren't here to party. We are here to fight bandits and thugs like the Thugee cult. They are tough and nasty and will torture you if you get caught."

That perked up our ears and quieted us down.

Sergeant I asked "How often do you think we will have a fight?"

The Sergeant had been in this country many years and said "You will all be going on month long patrols and can expect to run into several encounters with these savages. Keeps your wits if you want to keep your heads."

The rest of the evening was pretty quiet around the fire as everyone contemplated their personal futures.

*****

Sure enough, next morning we were told at morning assembly by our Lieutenant to get ready for a long patrol. He said it would last at least several weeks and possibly more depending upon what we found.

The next morning a platoon of us under Lieutenant Milborn setup with two supply wagons a few horses for the officers, and the rest of us on foot.

Our platoon was three sections of eight men each who were each under an experienced Sergeant. A signaler for the Lieutenant was also included.

We marched North and would camp somewhere with good visibility and water each night.

Sentries were posted and I did my share of duty.

On our fourth night out, I was doing midnight sentry duty when I got a bad feeling that something wasn't right. I looked around but didn't see or hear anything.

Finally, the feeling got so strong I woke the Lieutenant by nudging him under his blanket.

He woke in the dark and whispered "What's wrong private? I don't hear or see anything"

I said "Sorry to wake you but something is about to happen. I heard noises in the bush". This was a lie but I had to convince him to get up and wake everyone else-and I didn't want to tell anyone about my intuitions.

He said "Okay—let's wake everyone quietly". As we touched people we put our hands over their mouths to stop anyone from yelling.

Gradually the platoon woke and everyone put on their boots and reached for their muskets in the dark along with knifes too.

In five minutes everyone was awake and armed. We all moved to defensive positions.

Pretty soon we saw shapes coming towards us with swords and long knives in their hands. They thought we were all still asleep!

They sneaked to within twenty feet of the camp and then the Lieutenant yelled "Fire! Fire! Let them have it!"

There was a huge noise as everyone blasted at once. All the shadows went down but there were more coming.

The next wave of natives reached us and it became some real hand to hand fighting.

I was confronted by a middle aged native who gave me a dirty smile as he started to plunge a long knife into my heart. Fortunately, my intuitive sense gave me a few seconds warning so I was able to move out of the way and chopped his head off instead.

Other natives attacked our platoon and we were all fighting for our lives. I felt another knife slash near my back so I fell on the ground and twisted around to hit my attacker in the leg with my bayonet.

In a few minutes it was all over. We checked our perimeter for more possible attackers and made sure all the ones we had taken down were dead.

As morning dawned we were still all awake and in our defensive positions.

There were over forty dead Thugees who had attacked us. We had three dead soldiers and ten slightly wounded but who could walk and fight.

The Lieutenant got us all together and thanked me saying "Great fighting everyone. And Private Morgan was really sharp—he heard the attackers massing and gave us enough time to get ready for their surge. Private Morgan, you are hereby promoted to Corporal."

Everyone cheered "Hear! Hear! Great job Corporal" I was a little embarrassed and turned red but very happy to be recognized.

We all ate breakfast and packed up our camp leaving the dead attackers for the scavengers. We buried our own.

I kept getting thank yous and pats on the back as we marched. But I sensed that the worst danger was yet to come.

*****

We kept going on our patrol another couple weeks and came to the Ganges River in northern India.

Took a few days to rest near the river at a small town.

I kept feeling danger mounting but couldn't tell my officers anything since I didn't have any evidence.

Scuttlebutt was that the Thugees had a big concentration north of the river.

We took off from the river and headed north. After another day of marching we came to a cave complex.

Our outriders saw that people were in the Caves. They reported that it wasn't families but looked like the Thugees.

The Lieutenant had a plan for us to surround the cave complex then attack. I felt the touch of death and didn't want to be part of this attack.

But this was what I was being paid for. I also couldn't leave or I would be branded a coward.

*****

Lieutenant Milborn divided us into two groups. One to attack the eastern caves and one to attack the rest which were spread out all over.

I was in the second group. I really felt a deathly fear about this attack and knew we were going to get massacred.

Milborn signaled the attack. We all went in to start the attack.

We shot the first group of Thugees who came out of the caves wheeling their Scimitars like madmen.

But they just kept coming, and coming. I could see we were going to be overwhelmed and found a rock to hide behind.

So I took the cowards way out and hid in a crevice behind this large rock where nobody could see me. But I thought it was better to be alive and free than dead or captured.

Heard our men yelling and screaming. Then they ran out of ammo and it was all knife fighting.

After another fifteen minutes there was a quiet.

Then came cheering from the Thugees who cheered "Agga Agga, Wolind" over and over yelling at the top of their lungs.

I was very depressed because my mates and leaders were dead and I was alone.

I waited in my secure area outside of the cave complex until it was late at night.

Getting out of there when everyone was asleep I knew there were sentries to the south and wandering sentries looking for any more of us soldiers.

On My Own

I left my shelter past midnight and headed north, being guided by the stars.

Stopped occasionally when I felt the Thugees guards around and looking for anymore soldiers.

Finally cleared their area after five miles and kept going. Wanted to find shelter to rest and stay out of the way during most of the next day.

Found some logs near a river crossing which I could pile up into a protective shelter and disguised area for me.

Stayed there the entire next day and rested. Occasionally I would look around me and go to the river for water and to wash.

I had a few more rations in my pack but knew I would be out soon.

Fortunately my bow and arrow skills came into play.

I found some candidate spruces and after a few tries was able to shape a new bow. I used some twisted reeds to make the bowstring line attached to both ends of the bow.

Working in my shelter I was unseen and working on the bow and arrows kept me busy so I didn't have to think about my predicament.

As night was falling I left my shelter to go hunting.

I saw some shapes in the woods which became several raccoons as I crept closer.

The Psychic Soldier Series-Book 2-A Soldier is Born

I loved to hunt raccoons back in England. They were an easy target.

Creeping up on one I shot it through the heart. I really needed the meet.

Then I started striping the carcass and started a fire in the woods to cook it.

The cooked fresh meet was wonderful and I really needed it after short rations the last couple of days.

Also used the guts to make a better bowstring which would improve my bow and therefore future hunting.

The other thing great about using a bow to hunt for my food was that it didn't make the noise a musket did.

I kept the musket for future challenges but wanted to save the balls and powder as long as possible.

*****

Stayed in my shelter one more day to rest.

That morning I heard noises and saw a team of twenty Thugees crossing the river heading north.

This was not good since I couldn't go south through them and now they were heading north too.

I would have to move at night and use my senses to avoid them.

That night I set off on the dirt path walking north.

After several hours I felt I was getting close to the Thugees camp so I left the path and detoured through the woods around them.

Kept going another fifteen miles before I stopped. Wanted to gain distance on them and was looking for a separate way to go to get away from these savages.

The next day as I was peering out of the trees I saw a small village in the distance. Thought maybe I could get some supplies and more information.

Only got a couple hours sleep so I could keep going. In the early afternoon I reached the village and looked for someplace I could go.

Then I saw a small hut with a sign which was written in Hindi. I couldn't tell what it said but was drawn towards it.

Walking in the front door I saw lot of herbs hanging up drying and many bottles of what looked like medical potions.

An attractive but short middle aged woman came up to me and she spoke good British English "What can I do for you sir, I see you are a British Soldier on your own."

For some reason I trusted her and said "My entire group of soldiers was on a patrol and we were wiped out by the Thugees. All except me. I'm trying to find someplace safe to go. By the way how do you speak English so well?"

She looked me over with a friendly examination and replied "I learned English working for the British in Calcutta at the port. You are lucky you found me since I'm probably the only person in this village who does speak English."

"As to avoiding the Thugees, you have a real problem. They will learn of your presence here then track you down and torture you to death. You must get away soon. What is your name soldier?"

I said "I'm Corporal Morgan with an English Regiment. What about your name?"

She said "My name is Matana Virk. I am a healer. Let me think about what you should do…"

Her brow furrowed as she thought. She invited me into a back room and then heated and poured me some tea.

Finally her eyes brightened and she said "Corporal Morgan. I have an idea. But tell me first, how did you avoid being killed and how did you get here avoiding all of the people who might capture you or turn you in?"

I decided to trust her and said "When I felt we were going to lose the battle I hid behind a rock. Then I used my feelings and intuitions to avoid problems as I marched north."

She smiled and said "As I thought, you have already developed your intuition to protect you. You are very young to do this and it explains a lot about why you are still alive and free".

"You need to head to the monasteries in the Himalayas to learn more about yourself and to develop your abilities. This is where your fate is taking you"

I gave her a questioning look and said "Are you sure about this Matana? I'm just a simple soldier and have a natural ability which allows me to be more sensitive than others."

She continued "Yes I am sure. You have wonderful potential but have to develop it. This will be a long journey and through very tough terrain, so you will need to be rested and prepared. You can stay in my back room for a couple of days to rest and get ready."

I wasn't convinced, but it was a great offer and I really didn't have any other safe place to go.

I really didn't want to be a monk since I had heard that Christian monks were locked up for years and some never left their monasteries.

I said "Matana thanks for your offer of hospitality and I will accept. Not sure I want to go to the mountains and a monastery though"

She said "That is fine. You stay here for a while and I will tell you my story."

Matana's Story

After dinner that night Matana related her story:

"I was a young woman of eighteen who had a lot of compassion for other people's health.

I could look at them, see their auras, and tell if they were healthy or sick. (Although I didn't know what auras were at that time.) I kept quiet about my abilities because my people would have thought I was weird."

One day a Tibetan monk came through town. We all came out to see him as he passed his begging bowl around.

My mother and I were standing outside waiting for the monk to come down the road to us.

The monk was a middle aged kind of fat looking guy with a very loving smile.

He looked and me and my Mom and asked if he could stay with us that night. He said he had something to tell me.

My Mom agreed and so the monk did stay with us.

He told us his name was Sastra and he had been a monk for twenty years.

After introductions and pleasantries he said this to me "You child have many potential abilities. What do you want to do with your life?"

Replying, I looked straight at him and said "I want to be a healer to help people."

He nodded his head and said "You should develop your spiritual abilities and get some medical training too. There is a monastery a week north of here that has classes for laymen. They will train you."

My Mom said "Okay—but who would let her in and we can't afford anything".

Sastra leaned in a smiled "I know the Monk running it very well. I will write you a note and he will let you attend. The classes are for free—we just limit the attendees."

After talking some more my Mom agreed to accompany me to take a look at this spiritual school starting the next day.

When we got to the school after a week of travel it looked like any old brick building in a small town.

We stayed at the home of one of the women who helped run the place.

In the school I learned meditation and other exercises and became a true healer.

When I asked the teacher where all this knowledge came from he said "Up in the Himalayas there are places with much knowledge. What you learn here is just the smallest drip of what can be learned and abilities which can be developed".

Is this something I can do I wondered?

I asked about traveling there and the teacher said "This is not just a trip, it is a choice in life and would take you decades to learn. It is not a trip for a woman alone."

I accepted that because I wanted to stay in my village and get married. I just didn't want to make the commitment.

So after spending a year in the school (Mom went home after a month) I became a healer here and learned more about how to read auras. I also developed my healing abilities. Overall, it was a wonderful experience.

I've always wondered about making the trip and devoting myself to learning spiritual abilities.

This is why you should go into the mountains Corporal because I can sense you have many undeveloped abilities and they will train you there.

The Psychic Soldier Series-Book 2-A Soldier is Born

Into the Mountains

I thanked Matana for her story and told her I would like to rest now.

She nodded her head and led me to a corner in the back room with some blankets. I took a nap on while she fixed dinner.

As I was relaxing I thought about her story and thought the mountains and spiritual monasteries might be very interesting.

There wasn't an easy way to go back to the Regiment anyway with all the Thugees in between so I thought I'll just make a side trip.

The Regimental leadership would eventually decide I was dead anyway. They would probably also court martial me if I told the truth about hiding from the enemy or even if I didn't tell them the truth when I was the only one of the Platoon still alive.

I stayed with Matana several days to learn more about healing from her and then decided to make the journey.

Matana showed me some easy healing potions made from local plants and I came to really like and trust this older woman.

It was time for me to continue my journey and Matana gave me what I would need.

She gave me blankets, potions for health and endurance, and food. She also helped me get my boots fixed in a local shop as well as purchasing some other light foot wear for me to use when in a village or city.

I gave her a big hug and headed North out of the village on the trail. The trail kept climbing until I was breathing hard because the air was getting thinner. The forests became thicker the higher we went.

A few weeks later I was at the Indian border into Nepal.

There, I hooked up with a caravan going into the mountains by offering myself as a packer to pack and unpack the horses.

This packing was something I had learned to do in the army so it didn't seem too difficult.

Many people carried guns or knives to scare off bandits trying to rob the caravan so I was well respected for the weapons I carried and the caravan leader was happy to have me.

*****

We left the border in early August and headed up the trail further into the mountains.

As we climbed the scenery became more and more dramatic.

Soon I could see the whole valleys we had come from, and then later we could even see the Ganges over one hundred miles away.

We continued to climb and the weather got colder. I was glad Matana had helped me buy a winter coat too.

The vegetation started to turn into spruces as we climbed and the slow rivers below became smaller streams with rapids descending down the hills.

As the weeks went by we wound through little villages and often stayed in rooms in houses we paid to the locals.

Finally we came to our destination in Kathmandu. It was the capitol of Nepal and I was getting closer to my mountain destination.

The caravan leader Mr. Hondu thanked me for my help and directed me to the house of man who he said would be able to help me.

I said my goodbyes and walked through the city to find Mr. Nasim's home. I told the servant who answered the door that Mr. Hondu had sent me.

He Checked with Mr. Nasim and I was soon ushered to the Library.

There I met Mr. Nasim who was an older man with gray hair and wizened visage. He was reading an old book written in Sanskrit.

He shook my hand and I could tell he was a deeply spiritual person. I introduced myself and he motioned me to sit down. He said "Mr. Morgan you are a long way from home. Are you seeking something in our country?"

How could he know my name? I didn't tell his servant and nobody else on the Caravan had time to get here and tell him.

I replied "I was told by a healing woman in a small Indian village that I might find answers to my questions about myself and my purpose somewhere here in the Himalayas".

Mr. Nasim give me a close stare for a minute and I felt like he was looking into my soul.

It was an intense but loving look so I was not worried about him looking at me but more what advice he would give me.

He finally said "Mr. Morgan I've been looking at your Aura and focusing in on your future path." He said "You are a soldier right?"

"Yes" I replied. "I believe it is important to fight for what is right and I feel I have the skills to make a good career of being a soldier."

Mr. Nasim continued "Then you need to develop your spiritual side because that will also improve your abilities to take care of yourself when in battle".

"I don't understand why you want me to go to a spiritual center when I really just want to get back to my solders and friends as soon as I can."

He said "It's true isn't it that many men may try to kill you if you go back now?"

"Yes that is true."

He continued "Then some months or even a year detour may not really matter since the way back is deadly for now. You might also learn some useful skills to help you stay safe in the future."

"Yes that is true. I guess you are right. Can you tell me where I should go?"

Mr. Nasim got up and took down a map from a high shelf full of maps.

He opened it on a table and looked at various stars on the map on Nepal.

"What are those stars?" I asked. He said "Each star represents a monastery or school and I want to find the best one for you to attend."

He shook his head and got down another map of Tibet which also showed stars and some other Sanskrit symbols.

Then he smiled and said "You need to go to the distant Kingdom of Ngari. It is a long journey to the northwest mostly along a river. There are some lamas I know there who can teach you what you need to know. Are you up for the trip?"

I said "Sure, but a guide would help".

He thought a minute and said "There is a trader I know with a caravan which will leave this month for Ngari. I will talk to him about taking you."

He continued "I must warn you, it is a long and dangerous journey. Are you sure you want to go?"

"Yes" I replied with a nervous voice. "You said they can teach me things I should know and it can't be much more dangerous than what I've gone through already".

Mr. Nasim said "Great. You can stay here until the caravan leaves. I also want you to learn Sanskrit since it will be very useful to learn for your education in spiritual matters.

*****

Mr. Nasim did talk to the caravan leader who was agreeable when he heard about my offer to help work and my fighting skills.

The next several weeks were mostly taken up with studying Sanskrit while I waited to leave.

I learned that Sanskrit is an old language which goes back over two thousand years. I learned that it may be one of the oldest written languages in the world and the original Indian Vedas were written in it as far back as 2200 BCE.

Mr. Nasim introduced me to the "Yoga Sutras of Patanjali" which he said was over two thousand years old and which I would be studying in more detail in Ngara.

He said "There are four books in the Yoga Sutras and all are very condensed in meaning from the way you think about written books.

He held a heavy tome in one hand which he said was an English translation of the Yoga Sutras into English, then a small pamphlet of less than six pages which he said was the Sanskrit version of the book.

"See how efficient Sanskrit is to convey spiritual concepts while English doesn't have words for many of these concepts".

I started to learn the symbols which were strange looking and conveyed lots of meaning in each symbol. And learning a new language wasn't easy for me.

My teaching was also about learning how to write the symbols. I felt like I was in a grammar school all over again.

After several weeks of struggling to learn Sanskrit. Mr. Nasim told me it was time to go.

He also gave me something. "Here is a beginning book for children on Sanskrit and a copy of the Yoga Sutras. You will need to learn the language and how to speak it because where you are going since English is rarely spoken there."

I thanked him for his guidance and hospitality and left to join up with the caravan.

The Trip to Tibet

The road to Ngari was just a path which in places was like walking on a ledge and over deep canyons in some places.

It took a couple of weeks to cross Nepal and get to Tibet where we could start heading northwest.

The animals we saw included foxes, musk ox, snow leopards, and what was called the "Tibetan Blue Bear".

I saw all of these animals as we climbed in altitude from almost a mile high to over eleven thousand feet.

I started having fears of something attacking me. It came in my dreams and short visions while walking. But I couldn't see anything in my "visions".

One evening I was washing myself in a pond away from the caravan's camp.

I saw some rustling in the bushes and knew that there was an animal there watching me.

Stopped washing myself and took off running towards the camp.

Then a Blue Bear came running from the bushes chasing me.

I knew it was going to catch me and didn't understand why my intuition didn't give me more warning.

Turned to fight it when I saw that I wasn't going to make camp in time.

I tried to get a sense of where the bear would attack me but nothing came to mind. I felt psychically blind.

Slashed at the beast but he hit me and knocked me down. This bear must weigh over a thousand pounds so I felt I had been hit by a big wagon.

He started biting me and I felt horrible pain as he slashed me in the side and bit into my arm.

I was losing consciousness while I heard shooting from the caravan and the noise of help rushing towards me.

Woke up the next morning in a tent and thought I was going to die.

I felt burning pain in my side and my arm.

The caravan leader spoke some English and he leaned over me.

He was a thin older man with a balding head who like colorful scarves.

He said "Mr. Morgan I'm sorry to tell you this but we can't help you. Your injuries will kill you soon. We don't have the medicines or healers to help you. We will leave you here in the tent and hope you die peacefully".

I was in such pain that I couldn't say much. I just stared at him in pain and disgust.

In an hour I heard the caravan breaking camp and forming up. I could see a little through the tent entrance and saw that they really were going to leave me.

One of the caravan members came into my tent and took my musket. He waved and said "Sorry, Sorry..." I could see he thought I would die so wouldn't need the musket at all.

I was extremely angry about being left to die and I think that was a large part of the reason that I lived.

Struggling to Live

After living in pain for hours I realized I needed to get some water.

Using a branch near the tent I staggered and crawled over to the pond to get a drink.

It took me an hour and I felt like hell but managed to get there where I lay in the mud to drink some water.

Gasping as I made it back to the tent I remembered the healing potions that Matana had given me.

I lay down and struggled to get the potion from my pack then drank the whole thing. The small bottle was purple colored with a wooden stopper. It tasted terrible, like drinking dirt with peppers mixed in.

Then I closed my eyes to sleep. The trip to the pond had exhausted me and I needed to rest.

My sleep was very peaceful and the pain started to lessen.

When I woke again another day had passed. My pain was sharply reduced. When I looked at my wounds they were scabbed over and looked like they might heal without infection.

I would have some bad scars, but unbelievably it looked like I might survive.

Spent the next week hobbling around. Also made a new bow and arrows and shot some small game nearby. Squirrels and Raccoons. Also got one fox. Some the meat tasted gamey but I smoked all the extra to dry and preserve it.

After seven more days I was ready to continue to Ngara by myself.

Kept my bow slung and arrows ready in case I had to protect myself I continued walking the path.

It was slow going since my wounds still hurt, but the pain was bearable.

I hobbled up the path, and felt stronger each day.

There were occasional sheep herders who came the other way, but the trail was pretty quiet otherwise.

I was frankly shocked that anything could attack me and I wouldn't be able to anticipate its moves.

The only thing I could think of was that maybe some animals had a developed intuition too which would confuse mine.

The world was full of mysteries and I wanted to learn more about myself and the world I lived in.

*****

Over the next few weeks I was almost back at full strength and enjoyed looking at the mountains which surrounded my valley.

I had never seen anything like the Himalayas which climbed higher and higher.

Occasionally there were avalanches in the mountains which I could hear as a dull roar.

The trail went over several passes which must have been several miles high in the mountains.

I continued to shoot animals for food with my bow. Also did some fishing in a stream and caught a few local fish which tasted great grilled on the fire.

As I contemplated the intuitive bear that had attacked me I wondered more and more how I could have lost the initiative.

Something that Bear did confused me. It seemed that some animals had defenses against human mental abilities.

Could I find a counter? Was there a way for me to avoid a gap like this in my intuitions in the future?

I did not know the answers or what was possible. Another reason to reach Ngara.

*****

I was hiking one day up to a stream when I saw a snake on the path and it looked like a mountain rattler which is poisonous.

Even though it was dangerous I decided to test myself against the snake.

I wanted to see if I could anticipate a strike and move out of the way in time.

I moved closer until the snake started to hiss. Then I felt a strike was coming and moved myself in the opposite direction.

Sure enough the snake struck and it clamped its jaws into open air.

I tried again and anticipated correctly again.

Thinking maybe I didn't want to chance it again I walked away.

So my intuitive avoidance skills still worked. That Bear had just been an unusual case.

After another month on the trail I entered Ngara.

Ngara was a pretty large town with many caves over hanging the village and many acres of plants in fields being grown for food.

Searching the taverns and places to stay I found the caravan members enjoying themselves over food and drink.

I came in the door started walking up to them. When they saw me they turned white and started yelling.

They thought I was dead for sure. This was certainly a jolt in their lives.

Going up to the man who had stolen my gun I told him to bring to me immediately.

He was shaking when he took me up to their room and handed it to me.

Instead of getting upset or getting even I just left the tavern to find a place for myself somewhere else in the city.

I'm sure I gave them the scare of their lives and they probably still look over their shoulders to see if I'm coming to kill them. That was punishment enough for them.

The School of the Gods

I set out the next day to find the school I was told would teach me to utilize my abilities.

After walking around for hours I saw some monks begging up a street.

Gave some food to the monks and asked if they knew of any spiritual schools around.

One nodded and took me back to his monastery and introduced me to the Lama in charge.

The Lama was an old man but he spoke English. He said in a creaky voice "The place you seek is not here in town but up in the mountains. I can tell from your aura that you have many potential abilities and you need to go to the right school."

He used a wallboard to trace the route I would need to follow. It was a perilous journey up a nearby mountain.

Then he said "You must make this journey alone. They may not even accept you. To gain access you will need to wait outside the main gate—it might be for days."

"What is this place called" I asked. He responded "It is called in your language "The School of the Gods"".

*****

After a couple more days getting ready, resting, and with the proper supplies I started the climb.

Additional supplies in included ropes, food, and warmer clothing. I got rid of the bow and arrows and left my musket with the monks to lighten the load. Besides, I didn't think anyone or thing would be bothering more on the mountain.

I was told this would be a difficult short trek. A few more days to the mountain then a difficult climb.

The hike to the mountain was very pretty going along a small river in the valley. There were flowers and some lovely cliffs and rocks at the mountain.

The path was almost vertical in places. I couldn't imagine how supplies and construction materials were hauled up the slope.

I used the ropes to tie down myself and supplies as I rested.

Camped out on a ledge the first night and had a great view of the valley where Ngara was. Wished I was down there where it was safer since I was pretty nervous about the heights.

Next morning I also saw some metal hooks hammered into the rock and used my rope to hold me onto the narrow trail—which had a steep drop of several thousand feet.

That afternoon I came in sight of the School. It was a remarkable building.

There was a large Cave on the side of the mountain and the school was inside the cave. The buildings took up most of the cave which must have been over fifty feet high.

There was also a wall and timbers which leveraged out beyond the cave to extend the overall building.

I thought this place must hold hundreds of people.

Finishing my hike I arrived at the entrance which had large doors made of wood which must have been brought all the way up the mountain.

*****

I knocked on the door loudly. It was opened after a minute and I was motioned inside.

Inside it was fairly dark but there were lots of candles. A few small windows let light into the building.

There was an entry atrium with a small fountain with some birds in it.

I was brought to an older thin Lama. He was thin but healthy looking.

I greeted him and he spoke English too, but I could tell he was rusty speaking it.

He said "My name is Lama Gingding. Welcome to our school. Did you just want to see the school or do you have other intentions?"

I thought about it and said "I've been told by a healer and a wise man that I should attend your school to improve my abilities".

"What abilities do you have?" said the Lama.

"Well I have always had intuitions about animals and people. I'm able to tell which way they will move and if they will attack me or where they will go. There was one exception which I still haven't figured out. It was a Tibetan Blue Bear which attacked me" I said.

Lama Gingding laughed and smiled when he said "So you have met our Bears. Awesome aren't they? I'm sorry that you got hurt, but those Bears have much more strange about them than you know."

Then the Lama offered me a place to stay for the night and said we would learn more about each other in the morning.

They put me up in a small room with a window and small fireplace. In the fireplace animal dung fueled a fire to heat up the room.

There was a corner with blankets where I made my bed.

I slept pretty well, and heard a knock on my door in the morning. Opening the door I was motioned by a boy to come with him.

He led me down a hall and downstairs to the communal meal room.

There the monks were eating in silence. They were having yogurt and eggs with hot tea flavored with honey.

I sat and ate a good breakfast with them. Nobody even looked at me even though I was the only westerner there. After finishing I went back to my room.

Later that morning another knock and same boy led me to Lama Gingding's office.

The Lama looked up from his meditation in the corner and greeted me with a hug and a smile.

He took me on a tour of the school and it was amazing what I saw.

Apparently the Cave went way back into the mountain and I had only seen the bare outer layers.

Inside the mountain were areas exposed to the sky with crops and animals such as cows and sheep.

Holes in the tunnels which seem to have been enlarged over the years brought in sunlight and fresh air.

I was also surprised to see several streams which had been coming down the mountain and were now diverted through the Cave complex.

Multiple buildings had been built from bricks and mortar—often without roofs since they were inside the cave.

The Lama told me "We have more buildings than you might think in our complex. Some are classrooms, some for prayer or meditation, and some for residences.

Many of our Monks and students like their own places.

I decided that this complex looked pretty livable and not as cramped as it first seemed.

I queried "Who built this place and how long ago?"

Lama Gingding said "It was started thousands of years ago by wise ones who we are told still have an incredible hidden city somewhere on Earth. We don't know where it is but we believe it does exist."

I asked how many people lived there. He said "We have over three hundred people who live here full time and some transient visitors who come and go. Which are you?"

"I have already decided I want to stay. If you will have me."

Lama Gingding bowed to me seriously and said "We will be happy to have you. You will learn much here."

Going to School

In the weeks that followed I was assigned to classes, regular chores, and asked to teach English to those who wanted.

This meant I had a very busy schedule.

The typical day started with a Morning Prayer or meditation session in the chapel, morning chores and then breakfast.

After that were classes and then an afternoon break for everyone, followed by dinner in the evening.

My English class was after dinner five nights per week.

Some days during breaks I sparred with other students and monks-some of whom had learned Chinese Kung Fu techniques. I quickly learned I wouldn't do very well in those fights without knowing what they were all about so applied myself to learn eastern fighting to use my body more effectively than British soldiers ever did.

One of my classmates was about my age and had learned these Kung Fu techniques for many years before coming here, so he took me on as a student to teach me from scratch. His name was Numa.

In return for his help he attended my English class and I gave Numa additional language instructions as needed.

I had reached my eighteenth birthday by this time and was filling out into a strong and taller young man since I had gained several inches over the last couple of years and felt ready to do anything.

*****

The Psychic Soldier Series-Book 2-A Soldier is Born

My daily classes were a Basic spiritual class, one to learn Meditational Yoga, and one on reading, writing, and speaking Sanskrit.

In the basic Spiritual class I was with a lot of younger boys— some as young as six years old.

The monk who taught us wanted us to understand the theory of enlightenment.

He talked about illusions or Samsara and about Siddhis or spiritual abilities. He also made a lot of analogies to being an enlightened person and what that was all about.

This class went on for a couple of months, and then we were verbally tested on what we had learned.

My Sanskrit language was improving and I was able to take the test in that language-although I struggled a lot.

The next day, I found out I had passed and would be attending a more advanced class on spiritual abilities.

In my Yoga class I learned to go into deep meditational states through control of my breath.

These deeper mental states became better and better and I always felt much more rested and relaxed after them.

I thought of it as concentrated relaxation.

*****

It was also surprising to see that there were some girls attending classes.

This was uncommon even in England.

About twenty percent of the students were girls. I found out that most were Tibetans—even though many came from hundreds of miles away to attend.

Their parents were friends of monks and some were powerful leaders in Tibet and China. This school turned out to be one of the most liberal learning institutions in the country and was known among the powerful and spiritual as the place to train their children.

However, there was one western girl with dark black hair, who was taller than the other girls and who had striking features.

I had to find out more about her. We also had the same meditation class together.

We had said brief hellos together at the beginning and end of meditation class. I caught her at the end of one class and she agreed to meet me for dinner in the dining hall.

She told me a lot more about herself. Her name was Raina. "I was born in Greece and my parents were diplomats. I learned English growing up in school because it is used a lot in international diplomacy."

"How did you end up here?" I asked.

She looked thoughtful then said "My parents took us to Lhasa since my Dad was asked to talk to the Dali Lama and find out about business opportunities with the West. It was a long trip but we had top guides and military protection getting there."

"In part of the discussion the Dali Lama looked at me and said I had great potential and should attend one of the Tibetan Spiritual schools. He convinced my parents I would be safe and even sent extra guard with the caravan that brought me here."

"I'm surprised they let you go. My trip here was certainly not safe". I offered.

Raina said she had talked to her parents and since she was almost an adult they finally agreed. The Dali Lama personally guaranteed my safety to them.

She asked me and I told her all about my adventures with the British Army and making it here on my own. She was amazed by my stories and I felt really open and relaxed telling her all the details.

We ended dinner smiling to each other as we headed to our rooms.

*****

My life in the School of the Gods proceeded over the next months as did my relationship with Raina.

In martial arts fighting I learned how to throw someone away or over me and the sensitive areas on a person which could incapacitate them or kill them.

My instructor told me I was improving rapidly.

In the meditation class I was now getting the point where I could sit still for up to an hour and feel more centered in my spirit.

In the advanced spiritual abilities class I learned more about the basis for spiritual abilities.

The class instructor was a happy kind of fat old man who was very likeable name Mr. Tsao.

In his beginning lecture he told us this "How many of you have heard of "The Yoga Sutras of Patanjali"." Only a few people in the class raised their hands. I was one of them.

He continued saying "These sutras are written in Sanskrit and are several thousand years old. They describe how we all have a core spirit, and then layers of mind which cause our egos to think we are separate, and illusions which cause us to be foggy minded and not know who we are in the world."

*****

In addition to the regular class we also had one on one time with Mr.Tsao. In my sessions with him I learned a lot more about my intuitive abilities.

After me relating my intuitive experiences he said the following: "Mr. Morgan Our spirit is that which observes all things up and down the time stream because our core being lives outside of time and space.

When you calm the mind it is like slowing a swirling fishbowl and dirt settling to the bottom. Then the light at the center can see the surrounding world.

Your intuition comes from this connection of your mind to your core spirit.

As part of that connection you can see potential futures happening ahead of the events which allows you to make a decision."

To confirm what he was saying I asked "So the future actions I see is because of my connection to my all seeing spirit right?"

"Yes exactly" he replied.

So I asked "What about the part where you mentioned future probabilities?"

"Ah yes—the future is not just one thread, but a multiplicity. Your choices affect the future. Imagine you are riding in a boat down a river. You can move from shore to shore which represent different choices, but are bound by the river. The river might represent your world where the British Empire is dominant.

The Empire very hard to change because of the number of people believing in it so it has energy and momentum. But within that Empire river of fate there are many minor changes you can make."

Deep in thought I summarized "So you are saying the decisions I make can change the probable future for good or for bad".

"Exactly" he confirmed. "You can make different choices and you mainly have to deal with the momentum towards a particular fated decision." This decision can be changed through force of will".

He used this example "I once knew a man who had a dream he would drown if he crossed a river near his home and the boat capsized on the way across. Sure enough he went to cross the river and the boat tipped over. The people watching thought he was a goner because he could not swim. What they didn't know was that he had brought a float with him. When the boat turned over he grabbed it and was saved.

You could argue that he wouldn't have died at all, but the fact was the boat did tip over the way he dreamed. It was only because he had the foresight to bring a float that he lived.

So he changed the direction of the situation by what he did, and it had a positive effect."

I Thanked Mr. Tsao for his time as I had much to mull over.

What I learned was there was that there were not one but multiple actions we could take based on intuition and that we can have an effect about how events happen in reality.

The Psychic Soldier Series-Book 2-A Soldier is Born

Year Two in School

After being in school for a year I was becoming very comfortable with the environment.

I had learned a lot and developed all of my abilities much more.

My intuition had become a lot more sensitive. I did experiments with my friends on the limits of my intuition.

In an exercise room my girlfriend Raina stood in one part of the room and two other friends were elsewhere in the room.

Each person had a ball of paint and I had one too. Their job was to break the paint ball on me and I was supposed to attack and kill them with paint.

The twist on this was that each person was to randomly jump and move in different directions as they approached me in one situation then do exactly what they thought in another attack.

They were also to think about a specific path as they approached me.

The results were striking. In the normal attack where my friends thought and did the same, it was easy for me to avoid them and hit them back with paint.

When they made random changes from what was planned it was much harder for me to hit them.

I could still get some impressions but it was a lot more difficult.

My conclusion was that I was receiving a combination of their thoughts as well as actual future trends.

*****

The Psychic Soldier Series-Book 2-A Soldier is Born

In martial arts my instructor told me I had absorbed several years of instruction in one year and was now becoming a passable fighter. But it would still take me many years to become a Kung Fu master.

My relationship with Riana was that she would often stay in my room, and we tried to get away for time with each other.

We usually had one day free each week and sometimes we would go down the mountain to enjoy the fields and streams below.

Riana asked me an interesting question "You are developing many skills. What do want to be doing in five years?"

I realized I had not thought about it and mulled it over in my mind.

The next day I told her "I want to continue to be a soldier but also do the right thing. Not fight on the side of evil or wrong."

She was happy with that answer and kissed me. We both knew our lives had different paths but we want to enjoy our time together in school.

*****

Mr. Tsao organized a test for me. He said it would take a couple of days.

He and a couple of other monks took me down the mountain. We walked to a small cave near a river at the base.

Mr. Tsao instructed me "We have taken you to the home of a Tibetan Blue Bear".

When I heard this I started getting nervous. My only previous encounter with one of these Bears had nearly killed me.

He continued "This test is for you to put three colors of paint on the bear (which will wash off) without getting hurt or bitten by him".

"How do I do that? One nearly killed me last time as I've told you."

He said "Use your refined abilities to not only track the bear's thoughts as it moves, but focus on the probabilities of the future too. This will allow you to see the most probable moves the Bear makes to counter them."

I was sweating with trepidation but said okay.

Moving closer to the cave I realized I would have to go inside since the bear would not come out during the day except for good reason.

I crept slowly into the cave and could smell the Bear's strong odor.

Also heard heavy breathing. Apparently he was sleeping. Decided I wanted to challenge the bear in the open, not in the cave so I threw a rock at it and yelled loudly.

The rock hit him in the head and sure did the trick..He came awake with a roar.

Then he saw me and got up to charge me.

I did a quick backpedal out of the cave and into the sunshine. The bear squinted for a second at the light but followed me with an angry look. (If a bear can look angry).

I threw the first blue paint ball at the bear which hit it on the back.

If a bear could become even more enraged this one did.

It made a quick turn and charged me fast.

I felt the probability that the bear would knock me down with its right paw so moved left—even though it's right paw was out front.

It turned out to be the right choice since the bear did swing left and I was out of the way.

Then it moved towards me to bite, but I felt the probabilities that it would turn and gouge me instead.

So I moved back and then forward on the right and smashed another paint ball into its back.

Sure enough the beast had moved left and had tried to reach for me instead of biting.

I could see the bear was getting tired and it stopped to stare at me for a minute.

Then it started moving around me in a circle. It almost seemed human like. Who says bears don't think?

I looked at the probabilities and saw that the Bear would most likely rush me and try to knock me down then bite me in the chest from my left as I turned to face it.

So I waited until it charged, then moved back and around so it missed. I used the opportunity to turn so it missed me and through the third paint ball.

The paint hit the bear and I could tell it was tired so I ran fast to get into some rocks.

This tired Blue Bear decided I was no longer a threat so with a big roar saying that it had won it marched back into its cave to go back to sleep.

Mr. Tsao who had watched everything from a safe distance came up to me and said "Good Job. You have learned how to avoid the Blue Bear and keep safe from it. If you can do this with a Tibetan Blue Bear you can certainly do it with most people which are much less tricky."

*****

In my Sanskrit class I was now able to read most characters although some still gave me confusion.

I had read the full four books of the Yoga Sutras several times and got more out of them with each reading. It was originally written to allow the readers hours of contemplation and I did not disappoint the Author.

One of the things I learned was that Siddhis or Spiritual abilities developed as our spiritual connection to the God spirit grew. The books stated that the key for the seeker was to not become sidetracked by abilities but to stay focused on becoming more spiritually connected.

I debated these ideas in my advanced spiritual class with Mr. Tsai.

He told me that everyone has a different path and that my path may well flow towards the military as long as I kept spiritual truths in mind.

He was also a big believer in Karma saying that whether I did right or wrong, it would come back to me in this life or in a reincarnation.

*****

One of the subjects we covered were secret exercises to extend my healthy longevity.

These exercises had a lot to do with visualization and he told me if I followed them it would extend my life considerably. Possibly to multiple lifetimes if I desired.

After doing the meditations and visualizations he suggested I felt like my body was much more stable and healthier. Only time would tell if these exercises made the difference.

I would find out later that this truth about my longevity was one of the most important things I had ever learned.

*****

In my second year I was becoming more confident about myself and became convinced that I would acquire higher level abilities as I advanced spiritually.

Doing my daily meditational practices would help develop those abilities over time.

Additional practices could also be learned to implement new abilities like invisibility and shielding as needed.

Further, I had less and less desire to kill anyone even when they were trying to kill me so I made a personal vow to only wound and debilitate my opponents as much as was possible.

My instructors suggested a test for me to tell that I was ready to leave the school and continue my life's path.

They led me to a room deep in the cave. I had never been there before and saw it had many carvings and paintings of gods on the walls. The largest was a mural of Indian gods in scenes of war from the Veda. Portraits of Krishna and more.

They told me this room was only used to test students to see how well they had learned their lessons.

I was to be confronted by five monks. My challenge was to disable them or get them to concede to me when they saw they would die if I continued.

We all had long knives as we faced each other.

I knew that many of these monks had paranormal abilities and knew martial arts too.

This would be a big challenge.

Mr. Tsai did tell me that the monks would limit their abilities to what most fighters in the outer world knew but I would have a few surprises.

I looked at my opponents and they were all fighters I knew or had seen working out. All were quite formidable. I knew I would have to be at my best to win the challenge.

Mr. Tsai signaled us to start when he chopped his hand down.

*****

My challengers were all in a circle with me in the middle. I used my senses to feel their energies and probabilities.

They came towards me to touch me with their knives.

The rule was that a knife strike which drew blood would be considered disabling. Four knife strikes and I would lose the match. I had to disable them similarly.

I concentrated on seeing a path I could move through to avoid their strikes. It was barely possible.

I moved with all my energies to stay moving within the path and their strikes kept missing.

Then I slashed out lightly and caught three of them with blood scratches as I passed.

I stopped outside of the circle and they looked at me surprised before we continued.

After a few more minutes of these moves I was sweating but still avoiding the slashes.

The group attacking me in turn had lost two of its members as I had given them four slashes each.

Of the remaining three, two of them already had three slashes each.

The one left with no scratches was Numa, my martial arts instructor.

Thought I had this all figured out and would win when one of the two wounded disappeared!

I was shocked but knew he must still be in the room.

Felt for his aura just as he was about to attack when slashed him instead. He had four slashes and was out.

After I tagged the fourth fighter out it was just me and Numa.

We circled each other and I looked for an opening. I observed him like I had the Blue Bear down at the base of the mountain.

I kept looking at his probabilities and made an unexpected move.

Charging him I knew he would get one slash to draw blood but I hoped to draw three on him. One in passing and two as he lost concentration and became surprised about my attack.

It worked! I felt my first bloody slash from anyone, but left him with three blood trails.

Numa acknowledged my strikes with a nod then we went at it again. We traded strikes and I kept dancing out of the way. Then I made a huge jump into the air—one I didn't know I could do and got my knife under his neck.

He knew he had to concede. Numa did so then I received a round of applause from the others. It signified well done. I had passed!

*****

I was exhausted and had several bloody marks on me.

After I cleaned up and rested I was summoned to see Lama Gingding.

I entered his office not knowing what to expect.

He said "Mr. Morgan I see that you have had a fulfilling two years with us. You could spend a lifetime with us and learn much more but I sense you want to get back into the world. Is that so?"

I admitted "Yes Sir I have really enjoyed my time here and learned a lot but it is time for me to go."

"I thought so. We will miss you but everyone needs to follow their life's path. You will always be welcomed back here."

I thanked him and had tears in my eyes as I left his office.

That night in the dining hall everyone said their goodbyes to me after an announcement that I would be leaving the school.

It was a tough goodbye.

The Psychic Soldier Series-Book 2-A Soldier is Born

Raina stayed with me one more night but we both knew it was the end for us. We made love passionately and kissed goodbye in the morning.

That next morning I left happy but with regret. This school would always mean a lot to me and was a place I could almost call home.

Traveling Further East

I gradually traveled North and East following trails of animal herders and sometimes staying in their Yurts.

Over the next several months I gradually came out of the Tibetan highlands and into western China.

Learning some of the language and meeting travelers who knew what was going on I learned there were still many feudal warlords in this part of China.

This meant more opportunities for me as a soldier of fortune.

After a few more months of hiring myself out for manual labor and hearing local news, I learned where a warlord was who had lots of integrity needed more soldiers.

His name was Ling Yan and the trip to his domain only took about a week.

*****

I came to a stone gate with his soldiers guarding the entrance.

Using my limited Chinese I managed to tell the guards I was there to sign up to fight.

They looked me up and down and since I was taller and pretty well muscled they took me to their leader.

We walked up the road to an old stone fortress. From the number of people there I could tell me must have many hundreds of warriors.

I was introduced to the lead Ling Yan who was tall and heavy. He was obviously a tough warrior.

The Psychic Soldier Series-Book 2-A Soldier is Born

I learned that he often tested his new recruits himself.

He stripped off his light leather armor to just his lower pants and said we would fight with swords to see how good I was.

I asked what the rules were.

He said "It depends how badly I beat you. If it's too easy you leave my domain. If you last longer I will consider having you in my forces."

"What if I beat you Sir?" He laughed and said "If you do that you will be one of my officers! Don't plan on it though. Nobody has beat me in years."

Lin said "We will fight with real swords and you can get really injured with them. So be at your best and be careful."

When we had our swords ready we both bowed. We stood up and then he rushed me.

I could tell he wanted to injure my arm so I couldn't fight anymore. Therefore I step out of his way and tapped him with the flat of my blade on the back of his neck.

He was obviously surprised and circled warily with me. Next he tried dropping to the ground and kicking my legs out from under me. I saw this coming though and did a jump from Kung Fu training to get out of his way and sprang onto my hands behind his back.

Then I hit him on the rump hard with the flat of my sword-enough to knock him down. He grunted and got back up with blood in his eye.

He slashed towards me with a killing stroke which I parried. Then I took his sword from him with a wrist twisting motion and threw it to the other side of the room.

Ling calmed down, stared at me then, bowed and said "You are an excellent warrior and as I said I haven't been beat in many years."

I tactfully bowed and said "Ling Yan, there is much I can learn from you and your many years of fighting and leading men. So I would request you put me on your personal staff. I will obey you, learn from you, and do whatever you want."

He nodded again and said "Good. I like your attitude. You will be on my personal staff. You will start learning your duties in the morning."

"My aide will lead you to your quarters and I promise you lots of action."

I bowed again and said "Thank you sire, I will do my best for you."

Then his aide led me out of the castle and to some wooden barracks buildings behind the castle.

I was shown to a private room with a view of the fields in back.

A bell was rung later and everyone went to eat at a partially outdoor dining hall.

I was the only westerner there and got a lot of strange looks. Many of them hostile.

So I got in line with a plate to be served. A big soldier who everyone else moved away from came up to me and pushed in line in front of me. When I didn't do anything he started nudging me.

Then we got to the cooks ladling rice and they put some into my bowl. The large guy grabbed my bowl and said he was bigger than me and needed more food. I could see he was challenging me to embarrass me in front of the others.

I faked a punch at this tall soldier. As I did he turned to block me. But I was already sneaking to his right and knocked him hard on the back of his neck.

He turned again and I hit him in the face knocking him down and out.

Then I got back into line to get more rice. There were stares, but nobody said a word.

The Chinese Warlord

Ling Yan held a meeting of his commanders the next day and I was invited.

He stood over a map of his territory and neighboring warlords.

He explained his thoughts saying "As you can see from this map, we are surrounded by other territories. This would be fine except for the territory of Sun Madle who straddles the river which comes down through our land and waters our crops, animals, and people.

My observers have now seen that Sun Madle is damning the river to make a lake and keep divert all the water to his lands.

This will create a real crisis for our people and we can't let it stand."

He continued "I am opening talks with Sun Madle but we must also prepare to fight to save our land."

The rest of the discussion was about tactics in case we had to fight.

Several weeks passed and I watched how Ling led his people and his private army.

He was a good leader and kind to his people. As a warlord he knew his stuff and had great experience in conflicts.

I observed him as he sent envoys to Sun Madle's land and even a conference they both had where they met midway between their lands.

Ling tried to impress Sun about the importance of water from the river but Sun was arrogant and felt he had an overpowering army so he wasn't interested in accommodating Ling.

The talks broke down and it became clear to Ling and I'm sure Sung too that there would be war.

As part of Ling's staff I was sent to watch troops train and practice their skills at each other.

I was encouraged by Ling and his commanders to make suggestions.

One suggestion I made was about how the men aimed to shoot. I tried to convey to them to look for where things would go. Not quite premonitions but more observations about moving targets.

I created a real stir when I offered to show them by shooting birds. Had two birds released at the same time on each side of me.

Then I felt for the probabilities and shot into the space before the first one would reach it. Then quickly turned and aimed at where the second one would be in advance.

Both birds were hit and fell dead to the ground.

You could have heard a pin drop as the soldiers mouths opened and they stared at what I had done.

I followed up this example by working with the soldiers to setup launched targets. Then I helped the archers to shoot at two moving targets on each side of them. I worked to get them to shoot where the targets would go, not where it was.

None of them had ever tried to do this. They had only practiced on stationary targets.

As they practiced this naturally made their arrows more and more accurate.

Although Ling did have some muskets in his army. They were still very expensive so his men had to use all the weapons they could turn to advantage.

*****

Ling saw what I was doing and was impressed.

He put me in charge of a team of twenty five men to train and wanted to see what I could do with them.

We only had five muskets but the soldiers were all skilled in fighting with swords and in martial arts. We also had some excellent archers.

I thought about what I could do to make my team more valuable to Ling's army.

It seemed that Ling needed a special team to sneak into his enemy's location.

Making my team stealthy might increase their value to the overall campaign.

Telling Ling of what I was planning he wasn't sure of the value, but he let me proceed.

We started training at night. The goal was to get my team to learn stealth. I took them for hikes at night with full battle loads. It was as dark as I could make it and made sure there was no moon either.

Soldiers started by tripping and falling all the time until I taught them to use their peripheral vision to see around them using the more sensitive parts of their eyes.

They soon learned something I had practiced for years. Imagine walking through the woods using peripheral vision. Doing so you became more confident and could see plenty—certainly enough to avoid running into something or tripping.

After everyone was good at walking at night we did more practice on hitting moving targets. Both with muskets and arrows—in the dark.

Skills increased over a period of weeks until I was satisfied. Listening to Ling's meetings it became clear we only had a few weeks left until war would commence. This was because Sun's workers were almost finished with their dam.

Next I started on fighting skills. I trained my men to fight with knives and swords so they were more skilled.

Some of my men were pretty skilled but I beat them easily. Started teaching them how to plan to counter their opponent's moves ahead of time and they started to get the ideas.

It would take them months or years to really learn the concepts but I had all seen improvements in their fighting techniques.

With more confidence in my team I went to Ling with a suggestion.

My idea was to sneak in, plant gunpowder, and blow up the damn. This might avoid the entire war.

Ling stroked his beard and finally gave me a go ahead. He could see it would be much better to destroy the dam than having a lot of men die on both sides.

*****

Several nights later it was a moonless night and an overcast.

The Psychic Soldier Series-Book 2-A Soldier is Born

We could get onto Sun's land, but we needed to bring horses to carry all of the gunpowder needed. Keeping the horses quiet would be a challenge.

We put cloth coverings over the horse's hoofs to cut down on noise.

Packing up we were all nervous but excited about being able to do something which might stop the war before it started.

Then we took a long trail through the woods to end up near the dam. We started in the morning and ended up near the location late at night.

We got off our mounts and picketed them a half mile away to avoid Sun's men hearing any noise.

Then we took the heavy packs of gunpowder through the woods and snuck up on the dam.

Sure enough there were two groups of guards near the dam sitting around fires.

We expected the guards to be there. Waiting in the darkened woods, listening and watching we soon made out the guards.

It appeared there were about twenty men and five guards in hidden areas. A force about the same size as ours.

My plan was to get rid of the guards then attack the others quickly.

I sent out two man teams to knock out or kill each of the guards.

As soon as we received a bird signal that the guards were out we would attack the enemies with arrows. (The Guns were too noisy)

The Psychic Soldier Series-Book 2-A Soldier is Born

Our two man teams crept out and after ten minutes we heard the bird call.

I led our men as we attacked the guards in team one. We took them out with arrows silently.

Then we gathered our force to attack the second group. As we were about to attack one of their soldiers ran back to the fire yelling.

This led us to attack early with arrows. Some of the guards got down and took out their swords.

We ran into their midst and it started a big knife fight.

We soon had them all disarmed and tied up. We were all dressed in black with black face charcoal so they could not tell who they were anyway.

After they were all tied up we went and got all the gunpowder and brought it to the dam.

Placing charges all over the wooden and stone dam, we lit a fuse and ran to a safe distance.

The gunpowder blew up and it sounded like the end of the world.

Timbers and rocks were coming down from the air all over and we ran to get behind some rocks to shield ourselves.

The dam was totally wrecked and the water came rushing out in a flood. The water ran down the nearly empty channel and down to our lands and others.

When we got back to our castle Ling Yan himself was there to welcome us with smiles and slaps on the back.

He told us "Sun will know that we did it but won't be able to prove it. And he will not rebuild the dam because he knows we could do it again. Well done everyone. You have helped us avoid a war which would damage everyone."

I now had a lot of credibility with Ling's people but I was ready to move on. I was now almost twenty years old and wanted to do more with my life.

After another few months with Ling's army to learn more about how they operated I decided to take my leave.

Ling gave me a beautiful ingrained sword to take with me. I was truly grateful and he could see the tears in my eyes.

Travel Across the Orient

I was in far western China and wanted to go east. To see Japan… and maybe further.

Thought about how I could use my talents to make my way across China since I didn't have much money.

I decided to make myself look like a traveling monk. Since I already had much instruction in spiritual development I felt I could get away with it.

I was able to get a horse from Ling before I left as a reward for my services.

After leaving his lands I stopped in an empty grove of trees to put on my monk clothes.

They were made of wool and not that comfortable so I needed to get used to them.

*****

I was hiking the famous silk road which was the path used by ancient traders from the Middle East to China and back.

On this road I saw many traders from far and wide as well as military patrols and troops going east and west.

There were also some small groups of travelers which included families and other groups whose identities weren't apparent.

I occasionally camped near some other groups along the road.

One day I saw a group of ruffians threatening a family which was half women.

This was after everyone had stopped for the night and had started campfires.

The ruffians came over to the family camp and was pushing everyone around. Then they demanded payment to not bother them.

The Father-and old man who was thin and weak told them to leave them alone.

At this point these wild men grabbed a few of the women and threatened to take them back to their campsite and rape them.

This was the point I couldn't take anymore.

I walked over to the group and said in Chinese "I can't take your noise anymore. Please shut up and quit bothering this family".

Of course this immediately made me the center of attention.

The attacking group let go of the women and advanced towards me. It was a group of seven men who looked experienced in fighting.

All they saw in me was a young monk who was disrupting their fun.

The leader told me "Get lost. This is none of your business. I'm giving you fair warning"

They obviously didn't expect much of a challenge so kept moving towards me.

The family looked on in terror and some hope.

"I'll give you fair warning. Back up and get out of here and you will not get hurt."

This led to some growls and shouts and they charged me.

I pulled out my sword and started swishing around me to hurt them but not kill them.

After ten seconds I was still standing and five of them were on the ground with arms cut, slashes on their backs and several sprained arms and legs.

I said "Are you sure you want to continue? Some of you might die."

They saw they were outmatched and got up to retreat while shouting curses and threats at me.

The Father of the family introduced himself as "Tasir Malmade" and seemed very relieved "Thanks so much for helping us out. We would like to suggest you travel with us as long as our routes are the same. We would like to offer to cook your food and have you live with us. In return we would like your protection."

I responded "That is a very honorable offer and I accept". Truthfully I really liked their offer to cook for me since I didn't like my own cooking very much.

We continued along the Silk Road going east and stopped for a day every week or so to rest.

I got to know the women in Tasir's family and they were really nice gals. I enjoyed their company a lot but didn't want to get kicked out by the family or become part of the family so stayed polite and distant.

*****

The Psychic Soldier Series-Book 2-A Soldier is Born

I felt I needed some extra skills in case of more fights and I was thinking a lot about invisibility. This was a Siddhi talked about in The Yoga Sutras of Patanjali.

This skill would serve me well to hide from my enemies in an emergency.

I had read a number of invisibility exercises back in the School of the Gods but never had a chance to really practice them.

One exercise I learned was to relax into a meditative state. Then to send vital forces energy into the air around me. Then focus on creating clouds which would hide me. After the energy clouds were created I should then draw them to surround and hide me.

I tried this exercise several times over a week before I could see the clouds around me. On the fourth try I stayed calm and pulled the clouds to surround me.

I was meditating at a stream near where we stopped for the night and everyone saw me go down there to meditate. I practiced the invisibility exercise while sitting there.

Soon family members were coming up near me and calling out to find me and remind me that it was time for dinner.

They didn't see me! I wondered if this was real so I called back to them.

Suddenly they saw me and were shocked I was so close to them and they hadn't seen me earlier.

Anyway, it was all forgotten as we went back to the camp for dinner.

As I ate I wondered about what happened. So there was something about whether I wanted to remain unseen or not which affected my invisibility. If I made noise or drew attention to myself I would no longer be invisible.

I also remembered reading in one of the school's secret texts that not being seen by others was mainly about not being in their consciousness. That the techniques for being hidden were mainly about others having their attention diverted from the one hidden.

This meant I could probably go through a busy crowd and stay invisible but any attempt I made to communicate would make me visible.

I kept practicing my skills and tested how my skill worked as we kept going east on the road.

Occasionally I would excuse myself from the group to follow a call of nature.

Then I would spin my invisible shield and walk into the middle of a large group of travelers.

There was no indication they saw me. When I started a conversation with someone, they would be jolted because they hadn't seen me then decide they must have just not noticed me and they would calm down.

And that was the truth—what I was doing was diverting their attention to be able to see me until I drew it back to me.

*****

After another month on the road we ran into some trouble.

I started when we saw some troops—and I use this word loosely--marching down the road towards us.

We could see that they were bothering other travelers by robbing them or grabbing woman to kiss them or fondle them.

As they came towards us we saw them laughing and drinking. One of them saw our girls and came over to offer them a drink.

I stood in front of them and told them no. This only made them more aggressive.

They told me to get out of the way or they would kill me.

I said "NO" much louder and said "do not bother us or you will regret it" Maybe that was too bold because then about twenty soldiers came towards us.

I stood in front and pulled out my blade. They started laughing and attacked me.

Putting close to ten of them on the ground I told them there were easier pickings elsewhere.

They just laughed and continued going after me. I couldn't back down because I knew they would rob and rape my fellow travelers.

There had to be more finality in my resistance or they wouldn't quit. I decided to get serious.

I whirled around with my blade avoiding other blades, punches, and kicks.

In a few minutes there was a lot of blood and many of these wild soldiers yelling or dying.

This soon brought the attack to a halt and the officer in charge of them men told them to back up.

Then he looked at me and said "You have killed my men and I see we can't take you now, but when we get more forces you will be tracked down and tortured to death."

He got his men to hoist the bodies onto carts and they continued down the road. He also sent messengers in several directions.

I knew that I would have to separate from my friends since I was sure that the troops would hunt me down.

I gave my apologies to the family and they thanked me for their protection.

Then I took out jogging up the road going east to get away from the wild troops.

After another day on the road I could see that Imperial troops were scouring the road from both directions. I would just have to go invisible when they went by.

However, I kept tabs on the family I had been accompanying and was worried the troops would go after them.

Stopping occasionally I would watch them walk by while remaining hidden.

My worst fears were realized one day when an officer with a patrol saw the family and stopped them to ask where I was. The father Tasir Malmade said he didn't know. That none of them did. The officer said "That's not good enough" and ordered his men to take them prisoner.

I decided I would let them take me instead.

Made myself visible and said to the officer "Are you looking for me?"

He was shocked to suddenly see me and some of his men recognized me. They moved to capture me and I said "I will go peacefully if you release the family. Otherwise many of you will die."

The officer thought about it and he must have heard of how good a fighter I was so he said to watch me carefully—I was full of tricks. But he let the family go free.

I let them surround me and chain me too. This was not a good situation.

Prisoner

I was marched to the closest Imperial fortress which was a day's walk.

My captors didn't feed me but gave me a little water.

Frankly they were scared of me and it showed.

They stayed a distance from me since they didn't want to chance me fighting with them.

We reached the fort which had a guard tower and was made of wood and stones.

As we went through the gates I started to feel really worried. I wondered if I could get away.

The solders led me to their commander who sat in his large office in a kind of "Throne".

The commander was fat, with many scars, and he smelled like he had not washed for months.

He also had an evil greasy smile which I just didn't like.

I was pushed down to my knees while he talked. "So you are the rogue fighter who attacked my men. "

I said "They deserved it. They are undisciplined and were attacking other groups and mine on the road. They wanted to rape the women and steal from everyone"

He laughed and said "They are my soldiers and are allowed to confiscate whatever they need to keep them happy. So too bad. I think you need to have more respect for us. Take him away."

The Psychic Soldier Series-Book 2-A Soldier is Born

I was dragged to a room with lots of ropes, and other devices which made me think this was a torture room.

They hung my hands in ropes and pulled them up until I had to stand on my toes to keep my arms from hurting. They didn't give me any water and the room was hot.

After leaving me there overnight I was almost unconscious when they let me down the next day. Then they dragged me to a cell and I was locked in.

The cell was about ten feet square and did have an outside window with bars on it. It smelled like shit, which I knew must be the overflowing bucket in the corner. Wonderful.

I knew if this torture kept going I wouldn't be able to resist or escape. I would be too weak. So I had to make my move pretty quickly.

I went into a meditative state and put on my invisibility energy. After half an hour a guard examined my cell. When he didn't see me he raised the alarm and soon several guards were in the cell. I scrunched into a corner standing up—which was really tight— so they wouldn't run into me and find me by touch.

When they all moved to the side of the cell with window and the bars, I managed to move around them toward the door. Then I was out and they were still in the cells.

Looked for a water barrel or some other container. Finally found one used by the guards with a cup in it. Waited until nobody was near it then drank several cups of water.

Immediately felt better and decided what to do next. I decided to get even with the commander.

But I needed my weapons and clothes. Still cloaked I looked around and found them thrown into a corner with some other thefts from travelers.

It was quiet in that room so I put everything on. Then I waited till evening and went to the commander's main hall during dinner.

The Commander and his soldiers were eating dinner at a big table in the center of the room with servants delivering drinks and more food.

He was in a bad mood and was throwing chicken bones at his soldiers and cursing at them because I seemed to have gotten away.

I decided to appear right behind the Commander. Saw the other soldiers jumped to their feet and yelled as soon as they saw me. The Commander quickly turned around to see what was happening and he saw my sword right in front of his face.

He turned white but had the presence of mind to say "Ha you think you can kill me? You might but you will never get away from my soldiers. They will skin you alive."

I laughed, "Not likely- I am a demon who can kill any of you when I want to." I said to scare them all.

With that statement I made one big swish and took off the Commanders head which fell onto his plate.

Then I said to everyone else "I'm just starting to enjoy this. Who wants to be next?" And I cloaked myself to disappear.

The reaction was indescribable. They had seen me kill their commander and then disappear. No matter what the commander had said, they wanted out of there.

There was a lot of yelling and a general rush to the exits. I could distinctly see that some of them had wet their pants.

So much for the fierce warriors. I saw them all run out and took a leg of chicken to eat while I was leaving. Nobody was standing guard. It looked like they had all run into the woods.

So I made my way back to the Silk Road and turned east again.

In the Royal Court

Eventually the road led to Peking after another couple of months travel. Home of many dynastic Chinese Emperors.

There wasn't really much to keep me there but it was a famous city so I decided to stay for a week to see what the place was all about.

I took my own tour of the Forbidden City using my invisibility shielding to get into areas the public wasn't normally allowed.

Had a grand tour of all of the buildings including some the Emperor currently lived in.

Was just turning into an alley between two buildings when a man appeared in front of me. He was well dressed in Mandarin Ministerial clothes but didn't have any weapons.

He called out to me "Stranger. Are you having a good tour of the Palace?"

I was stunned because he was the first person to ever see me when I was using vital forces to remain invisible. And he knew how to become invisible too.

I said "Okay—you got me. But I will fight to the death to not be captured and tortured again!"

He looked very smart and had a nice smile. Then he laughed and said "I mean you no ill will. You are the first man I've seen who knows how to be invisible like me. Did you come from Tibet or India?"

More relaxed I responded "I was in both places. What is your name?"

"My name is Minister Valdasian and I am the Emperors Spiritual Advisor. You are welcome to be my guest for a while and I promise you will be safe" he said.

"That would be great. I would also be honored if I can learn more from you."

He nodded his head and said "Spoken like a wise young man in search of knowledge. Come, I will find you some quarters and then you can join the Royal Court for dinner"

I bowed and said "Thank you. I'm grateful to find such friendliness in Peking where I don't know anyone"

I also noticed he was wearing a copper medallion around his neck. I didn't know it then but that copper medallion would have important meaning to me in the future.

We proceeded to an area where guests and VIPs had quarters and I was given a wonderful room with female servants.

That night I ate in the main dining hall sitting next to the Minister. At the appropriate time he introduced me to the Emperor and I did the appropriate bows and said the right things.

The minister said I was sent to visit him by distant relatives in the hinterlands.

The Emperor welcomed me saying "We are having more contact with the West and I welcome learning more about our brothers there. Enjoy your stay and I hope we learn from each other."

*****

It turned out that the Minister had lots of time to himself. He suggested we meet daily to talk and learn more from each other. I agreed being very interested in what I could learn from him.

In our first meeting I shared my history with him and he was impressed that I had done so much in my young life.

Then he told me his story:

"I was raised in Southern China and my parents were merchants. We traveled many places outside of China."

"This included the countries south of China in the South China Sea. We also travelled to India. I was very excited by this visit to India since I had heard it was a land of mystery."

"Since I was a young man of twenty and very independent my parents didn't try to keep me in their caravan."

"Visiting some lectures by Gurus, I decided I wanted to become a wandering Sadhu to learn more about enlightenment."

"My parents disagreed with me but wished me the best as they left this area of northern India to trade on their way going east. I think they figured I would tire of the life and rejoin them."

"After a few years I ended up at a monetary in northern India which was known to have some advanced spiritual masters there."

"I listened to their lectures and learned to meditate."

"One day one of the masters happened to mention that he and other masters who had lived to over one hundred years knew spiritual techniques to vastly extend their lives."

"I asked one of the other students "Just how old is this master". He said that nobody knows for sure but that the master was reputed to be well over two hundred years old. This was amazing if true."

"Even though I was young I was very interested in these secrets because there was a lot I wanted to do in my life."

"Over time I was able to attend a class to learn more about longevity and life extension. This was with a group of older men in the monetary. After another year I started applying these lessons to myself."

Then he said "How old do you think I am?" I said "Hmm…" and looked him up and down. "You look about fifty years old."

He laughed and said "What if I told you I'm one hundred seventy five years old. I can't prove it to you but it is true."

I related that I had received similar longevity training in Tibet but because I was still young I had no way to confirm that it was working on me. He nodded and said "Good I'm glad you learned how to have a long healthy life. I'm sure we will meet in the future as peers."

Over a number of weeks I talked to other people in the Palace and they all said that Minister Valdasian had been in the palace in their parent's time. Nobody seemed to know how long he had been there.

Master Valdasian taught me how to read Chinese. I spent my days in the Palace reading Chinese texts, exercising, meeting with the Minister daily, and seeing Peking.

My travels were into the city daily to see the markets and meet people.

I even took a weeklong trip north to see the ruins of the Great Wall of China. What a fantastic construction it was!

Back in Peking I also found that my gorgeous female servants would also be available to me at night. This was a surprise, but since I was a guest of the Ministers it turned out that having servants sexually available to me was considered a perk for VIP visitors.

I wondered if I should take advantage of these willing women or not. I decided not to for now since it just didn't seem right to me.

In one of our daily meetings I asked the minister if he could teach me more about longevity and how to live longer. That I had learned some basic exercises in Tibet but wanted to learn more.

He asked me "Why do you want to live so long. You are still a young man."

I said "Well-I have a lot I want to do and see during my life and one lifetime doesn't seem long enough. I want to be on this earth for hundreds of years if I can to see more life and history. And I want to help people. It might take me a long time to really make a difference."

He said "Okay, that is a reasonable thought. I will start teaching you about longevity going forward."

Longevity

What I learned from Minister Valdasian over the next months was amazing.

There were many things he taught me about the aura including seeing people who were hidden—but their life force was showing. This is how he saw me the first time we met when I was invisible.

He taught me that extended Longevity was not one magic thing. It was multiple aspects of our life.

He explained "Extended Longevity is all about integrating Spirit, Mind, and Body. That one has to learn how multiple factors affect our longevity to be able to extend it."

"You need to exercise regularly, eat the right foods, and learn how to manipulate your vital forces. But the biggest thing you can do is to build your spiritual connection."

What does that mean I wondered "What do you mean by me building my spiritual connection?"

The Minister said "In deep meditation I will teach you to visualize how to bring a blueprint of life down into your body. This will let you stay young and become younger. This is the key to living a long healthy life—your spiritual connection. All the other things you can do are important-but none more so than building your spiritual connection.

*****

I had much time to reflect and think about my future. Did I want to live a long life? What was my purpose in life? Where did I want to go and what did I want to do? Did I want power and women?

… Or something more spiritual in life.

I knew that I wanted to do good. Wanted to help people. This went back to my growing up in Wales. My parents took me to church every week and tried to teach me to be a moral and ethical person who lived by my personal integrity.

Liked the concepts of enlightenment, but they didn't really hold me enough to make searching for enlightenment an important priority in my life.

I started thinking about what it meant for me to be free of the normal expectations of my environment. In other words to have "Personal Freedom" in my life to make it more worthwhile.

What was "Personal Freedom"? To me it seemed to be the idea that I would have many many years to do whatever I wanted and to reach my purpose(s) in life. That I could travel the world and experience all that I wanted. That I could help people in many ways. This was what I wanted to do.

*****

The Minister asked me at our next session what I hope to gain from learning Immortality. I was glad I had thought about this question previously.

I told him "To me it's all about Personal Freedom. If I know that I can have many professions, see many places, and help many people it will help me feel unbounded. To be able to not feel tied to a particular lifestyle or place. To know that I will not be limited by time in my life. That will be a great freedom for me."

Minister nodded his head and I could tell he liked my thoughts.

Thus began my training in many deep meditational techniques and in learning various principles which would help me be healthier, live longer, and be happier.

*****

I could tell the Minister was hiding other advanced secrets he had learned.

I told him so "Minister, I can tell you are very highly developed and you show people only a small portion of what you know. Please show me what you can do."

He smiled and thought about it a minute then said "Okay, I will show you a few things but you must understand about this too. You will not be able to develop these abilities for many years, probably well past a normal human lifetime. Also, these abilities of Siddhis are a side effect of spiritual development. Your spiritual development is more important than these abilities in the long run and Siddhis can be distracting."

"Do you understand what I'm telling you?" He asked as he stared at me.

"Yes—I understand. Siddhis are developed as our Spiritual connection develops and as that happens we have more respect of others and less willingness to use force against them. That is the dilemma for me. As I develop I will want to be a soldier less and less. I will have to choose carefully about using my warrior skills or it will hurt my spiritual development"

He commented "Yes, that is correct. Also, you will accrue bad Karma if you treat people or even animals badly."

I said "I still want to see what you can do"

He smiled, closed his eyes, and there was a "pop" in the air where he had been. I was becoming pretty sensitive and could tell he wasn't just invisible. He wasn't in the same space anymore.

I jumped from where I was sitting and looked around. I saw a glimmer in the other corner of the room and he solidified there out of thin air.

My eyes bugged out and I said "I don't believe it. It must be a trick. You were not invisible. You actually moved in space."

Then he walked towards me with a peaceful attitude and took my hand.

Suddenly we were outside of the palace and in a dark alley. We walked out of the alley and were in a local market I recognized.

I was too stunned to say anything. What had he done? Was it really possible to move from place to place instantly?

Soon, we were walking back towards the palace. After I regained my presence of mind I asked him. "What did you just do?"

He said "I just showed you the Siddhi of Teleportation. It is difficult to learn and most people don't learn it until they are well over one hundred fifty or even two hundred fifty years old. So don't expect you to learn this in the immediate future. However, if you live a long time and build your spiritual connection you may possibly be able to do it."

I thought about what an amazing ability Teleportation was. It could rescue me from many emergencies and would allow me to do incredible things.

I asked him "Did you ever use this ability when in danger?"

He said "Yes-Many years ago I was cornered in an old house but was able to continue firing arrows to keep my enemies out. They started burning the house and I knew I would be done for. So I sat in a meditative position and practiced the Teleportation exercise I had learned in India.

After ten minutes the smoke was becoming thick and the house was about to fall on me. I reached the right mental level of focus, and suddenly I was near a stream I knew and visualized several miles away. Then I was able to marvel over my escape and soon headed in a direction where I would be safe."

*****

The longer I lived at the Palace the more in awe I become of Minister Valdasian. He was a true spiritual light and I could see why the Emperor retained him to help him with his own personal issues.

The Minister helped heal people too.

Once I saw a soldier brought into the Palace who was a nephew of the Emperor. The Minister was summoned and as his helper I tagged along.

In a quiet room the young soldier was laid on a bed and the Minister came to look at him.

The soldier had been shot by an arrow in the chest. Although the arrow had been removed, there was a hole which looked deeply infected with red streaks running from the wound.

The Minister went into a meditative state and laid his hands on the soldier's chest. After a few minutes I could see a white light from his hands going into the wound. Soon the infection disappeared and the hole started closing.

The Psychic Soldier Series-Book 2-A Soldier is Born

The soldier was breathing easier and the Minister said quietly "He will heal now. Let's leave quietly so he can sleep."

A few days later the soldier was at dinner with the Royal Court when the Emperor rose and acknowledged the healing. He said "Minister Valdasian has performed another miraculous healing on my nephew. The Minister is a great man and knows that whatever he wants this Emperor will provide."

The Minister got up and bowed to the cheers of the gathering. He said "My only wish is to continue to serve the Emperor and Royal court for the rest of my life." This statement was greeted with even more cheers and a nodding head from the Emperor. Then the Minister sat down like this was an everyday occurrence.

*****

Although I enjoyed the Palace life for six months. I started feeling that tug in me again which meant it was time to start moving on.

I knew my mission in life meant I had a lot more to do and see and that the side trip in Peking was to help me learn but that my future led elsewhere.

The Minister sensed my mood and understood that my time to leave was coming.

He gave me a crystal to keep and said that focusing on it would help me to know what I should do in a particular situation.

He also told me this "I can see that you have many more things to learn and accomplish in your life. You will live a long time like me…maybe even longer."

I said "I am grateful for your time and instructions Minister. Is there anything I can do in return?"

He replied "Just continue to learn, build your spiritual connection, and do good in the world. The world needs more good and able people." I bowed and thanked him. He was one of the really bright lights in my life.

*****

So I left the Palace after saying good bye to everyone including the Emperor. I told him how much I had enjoyed staying in his palace and that I would tell everyone on my travels about the great and wise Emperor of China.

He was very happy to hear this and gave me a bag of gold coins and a royal scroll to enable my journey.

The Psychic Soldier Series-Book 2-A Soldier is Born

In Japan

I decided to head towards Japan because I had heard many interesting things in China about that country. Many of them bad because of the wars China had fought with Japan.

But I recognized it as a different but powerful culture and wanted to learn more.

I found a trading ship in Shanghai and with my gold coins bought passed to Japan.

The journey took a week then we entered the port of Yokahama in Japan.

In the Harbor I saw a large number of British and other European ships.

Should have expected it but I was now back in the midst of westerners who were in Japan for business and trade. Some military ships were here too. Mostly to perform services for the government.

Going onshore I looked for a western Inn and found one near the harbor full of sailors. It was called "The European Trader".

Got a meal in the main room including some good old British Grog and some well cooked beef.

It was great to have western food again. I really savored the drink and the beef.

The noise was loud with many drunk sailors. One of them was a big Irishman who kept shouting insults at me. I tried to ignore him but he got up from his seat and came over to me.

He continued in his rude language "What have we got here. A weak little piss ant who looks like he is all dressed up in Chinese trash clothing." as he put his hand on my shoulder.

I twisted his hand hard and he quickly went down on the floor. He became red faced with drunken anger and roared "I'm going to kill you." So I twisted harder then put him in a chokehold until he was unconscious. Then I let him gently down to the floor to sleep it off.

Brushing myself off I ordered some fish and chips.

The room had been quiet. Suddenly the room started talking again and everyone ignored me like this happened there every day. Maybe it did.

I took a room at the Inn, put a dresser up to hold the door closed and had a nice long sleep.

In the morning I went to the main bar and meal room downstairs to find out what was going on of interest.

A few sailors were eating breakfast from the previous night and waved me over.

One laughed and said "You sure put the kibosh in Mickey last night. He deserved it."

"Thanks" I said "I didn't mean to hurt him but he was really annoying."

They said "Yes-He does that—and I'm sure he is sorry. He will not hold a grudge and probably won't even remember what happened."

As he said that Mickey came lumbering up to the table and sat down. Everyone could tell he was nursing a big hangover.

I was tense but then Mickey spoke up. "Ugg, I have a real headache this morning. Does anyone know what happened to me last night"?

Everyone looked at each other. One of the men at the table spoke up and said "Yes you got all drunk and went to the alley way where you were attacked. This nice young man went and helped you to fight off the attackers and led you to your bed".

Mickey looked at me and said "Thanks young man. I'm in your debt and would like to return the favor sometime.

Everyone else was trying hard to keep from laughing. One person started choking on his food and got up from the table to go outside.

I took this all in stride and said "I just got here and am looking for work. If anyone has any ideas I'd appreciate your suggestions."

They asked me what I did and I said I was a soldier with some battle experience.

Most of the table nodded their heads except for Mickey who said "You look kind of thin are you sure about that?" This led another couple more sailors to cover their mouths and get up from the table covering their laughs.

I kept calm and said "Yes I am experienced. Any suggestions?"

Mickey and the remainder of the table thought about it and said "Well, we know the Japs are hiring soldiers. They are always fighting little wars.

Mickey snapped his fingers "There are a lot of religious missions in this country. I know of one upcountry a hundred miles which gets raided all the time. I hear they are looking for some soldiers to protect their location from bandits."

This seemed ideal and I thanked him. As I got up from the table I said to Mickey "Thanks for your advice. I would rather be up country fighting bandits than taking on anyone like you."

Mickey replied "Yep I'm a top soldier and am sure I would make a pretzel out of you pretty quickly." I nodded and responded "Yes—I'm sure you would."

This led to general laughter at the table as I said goodbye and left the happy sailors.

The sailors all waved me bye with mirth in their eyes.

*****

That day I packed up, bought a small pony and started up country to the Scottish Christian Mission.

Also started practicing my Japanese and had bought a small translation book in Yokahama. It helped that I also met other westerners on the way who could help direct me.

After about a week on the road I was walking on a remote road when several Samurai came out of the woods. I knew they were Samurai because of descriptions I had heard of them in Yokahama.

I was told they were very dangerous soldiers and sometimes turned into bandits when they didn't have a master. Then they were called Ronin.

The one who seemed to be the leader motioned me to throw down my pack. I did so immediately because I needed to be freed up to fight.

The leader looked hard but seemed intelligent. My intuition told me he was a solid soldier down on his luck.

The two other thieves looked tough but nasty. I sensed they would kill anyone just to steal their stuff.

They motioned me to get down on the ground while they searched my pack. It was a given that they would take my horse.

As I bent down towards the ground I whipped out my sword and hit one of the samurai. He was fast and managed to jump out of the way. But I also knew he would jump that way and twirled around to slice him in the guts as I turned. He went down yelling in pain.

Then the other soldier attacked me with short knives and I spun to knock him off his feet.

The older one made a few slices with his sword at me and I avoided all of them while getting behind him where I grabbed his throat and stuck my knife under it.

The older and wiser Samurai looked back at me in surprise and pain. He said in broken English "You are not just a normal traveler are you?"

I nodded and said "No" as I let him go and went into a defensive position facing my two main attackers. "I am an experienced soldier with many additional abilities. You would be wise to avoid me."

The leader said "Yes I see." And he put his sword away and bowed down to me. His friend saw what was going on and put his knives away and bowed too.

The leader said "I am senior Samurai Tsonga. My friends Nitge, and Calmo. We have been starving Ronin. You killed Calmo so it is just Nitge and me now. We need a new leader and I can see you might be the one. Do you wish us to follow you as your warriors?"

I was shocked to hear this but I said "Yes—I'm going to a Christian Mission site and they will need additional soldiers there. Do you want to come?"

Tsonga nodded his head and said "Yes—you are an extraordinary fighter and we will follow you. I sense great things will happen being part of your retinue."

So Tsonga, Nitge, and I headed up the road for the next couple of weeks.

We got to know each other and I learned that they had been soldiers of a great warlord who fought many battles. They worked for him for most of their adult lives.

When there were no battles they had homes and wives as part of his army. Then the leader died from disease and his heirs didn't want as large an army. So all three of them were fired a couple of years ago. They had been roaming the land since and had recently turned to banditry for food but really hated it.

The Christian Mission

We finally reached the Christian Mission after another week on the road.

It was a group of several wooden buildings including a small church which could hold about fifty people.

There were also some fields with vegetables and crops to help feed the group. A few milk cows roamed the fields.

We went to the entrance and were greeted by a young woman who really caught my eye.

She was dark haired thin and curved in the right places. She was also tall.

She greeted us with a Scottish Brogue saying "My name is Brianna. Welcome to all of you. You are welcome to stop here for food and rest."

I said "Thank you, we have been on the road a long time and your place looks like a really nice place to stay. We are also looking for work."

Brianna said "You should talk to my father about work. Come on in."

We were given quarters in a type of barracks for men. It was warm and dry which was all we needed.

We were all invited to dinner that night where we had a chicken stew and vegetables grown at the mission.

After dinner the leader Minister MacAbhra invited us to sit with him in the living room next to a fireplace.

He talked a lot about his mission "We have been here ten years, and built a lovely place which is a source of godly inspiration for the locals." We all nodded our heads in agreement.

"But in the last year or two there have been many more robbers and Ronin in the area. We were already robbed one time last year and were scared for our lives. Fortunately the gang mainly wanted food."

"So I'm looking for guards for our mission. You all look like you are used to protecting yourself and maybe fighting others" he said.

I volunteered to speak for the three of us "You have a good eye Sir, we are all soldiers and have lots of experience. We are also looking for somebody to work for. We just want to feel useful."

Minister MacAbhra looked at us and thought for a minute as he smoked his pipe.

Then he said "I think I can use all three of you. I can't pay a lot but the job includes lodging and food. You will need to protect us from raiders and occasionally help with other chores. Is that acceptable?"

I looked at my Japanese Samurai friends who nodded then said "Thank you Sir we would be very happy to accept your offer. We will need to make some defensive additions to your Mission to make it easier to defend."

He said "That sounds great. We will look forward to you joining us in the morning." And he shook all of our hands.

*****

The next morning we started our jobs to enhance the security of the mission.

After a good tour of the place we noticed several places which could be better defended.

There was a stream around two thirds of the property so we decided to build a fence with spears sticking out from it and a few gates. It would take us a few months but we got started by setting stakes to mark post hole locations.

On the rest of the property we wanted to dig a trench and build additional fencing.

I approached Minister MacAbhra to show him our plans and tell him that having some native labor would help a lot and let us finish the fortifications more quickly.

He nodded, asked questions, and said "Yes-This sounds like a good plan. We can get some cheap Japanese labor from the villages nearby and I think most will be willing to work for food."

I also went to the house with him and showed him where we should add shutters and other improvements to the doors and walls to make it more defensible.

The Minister agreed with our work and just told us to do it quickly because Spring was coming in a couple of months and that was when most of the hungry attackers arrived.

My two compatriots and I set to work with a will. We each worked to manage the local workers on different parts of the project.

The wall around the compound and gates were the highest priorities.

With an additional twenty local workers they helped us build the project quickly.

The Psychic Soldier Series-Book 2-A Soldier is Born

We had teams digging post holes, cutting posts from the nearby woods, making spears, and building the wall. The wall was ten feet tall with sharpened posts at the top.

The idea was to just make it difficult to attack us anywhere except through the gates.

There were two main gates. The front, and the back. We fortified around the gates with bolt holes which we could use to shoot muskets or arrows.

In the house we built internal shutters for the windows which could be used to bar windows from the inside.

The doors were reinforced and had wooden barriers which could be used to keep the doors from being bashed down from the outside.

Within a month, the outlines of our defenses were taking shape, and our tactics to defend if attacked.

My samurai and I also took a trip to a city with a wagon to buy more muskets, powder, and balls. The Minister trusted us and I was not going to let him down.

*****

After two months we were nearly finished with building defenses. We had also trained some workers at the mission and some locals who had help with the construction to help us defend the site.

Then began the waiting. We helped out with chores and weeding of the fields while waiting for the bandits.

It was several more weeks before we had raiders. Three raiders rode up to our gate.

The first thing I noticed while watching outside the gate one sunny morning were several Ronin riders outside the gates. One came up to me at the gate and said "We need food. Can you help us?"

I replied "You are welcome to get some food inside if you drop your weapons outside first."

The Samurai was dirty and had mean eyes. He said "How dare you tell us to drop our weapons outside. We are Samurai and don't do that."

I said "That is the only way you are coming in here."

He looked me up and down and could tell I was not an easy mark.

"We will be back and then you will die" he said. Then they rode away.

I told the Minister about the incident and that they would be back with more Ronin.

He agreed and said "Well, I hope your defenses work. Keep up your good efforts."

*****

I should also mention that Brianna and I were becoming good friends. She was lonely and I was the only other western male of her age in the compound.

We went for walks together to talk and sometimes to a local swimming hole. Being a very proper woman, we didn't do much more than hold hands but I really appreciated her company.

Brianna promised to stay in the mission or not go out without one of us guarding her.

The Psychic Soldier Series-Book 2-A Soldier is Born

*****

A few days later a larger group of fifteen raiders rode up to the gate.

I ran to the gate to talk with them. Their leader was bald and looked like a real fighter. I was concerned about him since my intuition told me he would be difficult to beat.

He looked at me and spoke "You look like a worthy warrior but my spies tell me that the rest of the people here are soft. Why don't you join our group and we will take what we want here and then go to other villages to pillage in the area."

I smiled evilly and said "I don't think so. Your group looks like a group of tired whores and we will protect our mission. I said this in Japanese and everyone heard.

There were a few mouths open and lot of cursing with many hands on their swords.

The leader said "Okay-we will go." And he started to lead his gang away from the mission.

Then he yelled and made a pre-arranged signal.

They broke up into two groups. One for the front gate and one headed for the back.

Fortunately, I already had my two Samurai watching the back gate with help from the Mission and locals.

At the front gate I had five people to help me. I was counting on them to shoot arrows and two muskets.

The leader's group charged the gate on their horses.

I told the men to shoot at the horses to knock them down and then at the riders.

Several horses fell while I shot my arrows at the attackers. Most of them had leather armor so I had to aim at the joints.

Two of my arrows found necks and those people fell of their mounts and were silent.

One of the horses fell and crushed his rider.

So out of the eight at the front gate I faced four.

Several of them charged me and I quickly sliced them down.

This left the leader alive and steaming at me. I could tell he really wanted to kill me.

I waited for him to charge me which he did after jumping off his horse.

He was better than me with his Katana sword and I had to back up a lot.

He made another thrust which I parried, then I swung around to catch him in his side, but he blocked that too.

Now I was sweating, this guy was really good. I wondered if he had some intuition too.

Out of the corner of my eyes I saw my Samurai friends coming towards us from the back gate coming nearby. They must have already beat their attackers.

The leader also saw this and instead of retreating he doubled his efforts. I could tell he wanted revenge on me for destroying his gang, even if he was killed in the process.

I tried to think of what else I could do to win. I had to show my skill and not have my friends help me.

This Samurai was a great fighter. I called a truce to our fight by insisting I wanted to talk for a minute.

The gang leader agreed to listen. I could tell he wanted to rest for a minute anyway.

I said to him "Look we have decimated your gang and I know you want to kill me. Let me offer you a deal.

If I can get you to surrender our fight will you give up your gang ways and give me your loyalty?"

He laughed and said "Ha I doubt that, but if you do I will."

With that we started our fight again.

He made a big swing with his Katana and sliced my armor. I could feel a sting as he drew some blood in my chest. I was more stunned than hurt.

I focused on my intuition and twisted to hit his hand hard and knocked the sword out of his hand.

He was shocked. Then I put my sword to his neck and said "I win. Give me your loyalty." I waited a tense minute while I saw his anger change to admitting his defeat.

Finally, he said "You are a great warrior. Nobody has ever beat me like this before. I give you my loyalty."

I looked into his eyes and saw he was serious. I asked him his name and he said "My name Ramanda."

Dropping my sword I took his loyalty oath with him handing me his sword with both hands. I took his oath and handed the sword back.

So we won over one of the largest gangs in the area.

*****

Word got around not only the local villages but to neighboring cities that we had beat a large gang and I'd take the loyalty of the leader I beat. Ramanda had never been beat and had a big reputation as a soldier.

At the Mission we felt safe. No other gangs in the area had any interest in attacking us after we killed Ramanda's gang.

I was also really impressed with Ramanda's sword fighting skills so I wondered if he would give me lessons. The only reason I bested him before was because of my intuition advantage.

I asked him if he would teach me and got a confused look. He said "You already beat me. Why would you want me to train you?"

So I setup an experiment where I told him to hit me from behind.

He stood behind me and aimed a big kick to my back. When I sensed the kick was coming I just moved to the right and he missed. After a couple more attempts to attack me missed I explained that I missed him using my intuition of where he would be. But his sword fighting skills were much better than me.

He finally understood what I was telling him and he agreed to teach me.

We practiced once a day and he started with the basics on how to hold a Katana Sword.

Then we proceeded to basic exercises.

Finally we did sparring with swords to test the new skills he was teaching me.

I realized that everything I had previously learned about using swords from the British Army and my fighting experience was wrong.

That I would become a much more effective sword fighter with this new training. This was great because I wanted to learn how to use many types of weapons.

In my sparring with Ramanda we used wooden swords and the contest was to see who could get the killing advantage the fastest. Gradually I got better and better to the point where I was winning most of our matches without using my intuition.

At that point Ramanda said he didn't have anything new to teach me.

*****

Brianna and I become closer as I lived at the Mission for over a year.

I could tell she wanted me to stay and maybe even marry her. I loved her a lot but I also had itchy feet. My direction was to see more of the world and I had to tell her.

So one day I took her to sit under our favorite Oak tree. She could see I was troubled and nervous when I held her hands.

I told her "Brianna. I really love you but I have more of the world to see."

She said "Where?" I told her "I'm thinking of going to America to just travel around." She stared at me and said "Don't you want to settle somewhere like San Francisco?"

I said "Maybe someday, but for now I just want to see more of the world."

This was the nineteenth century remember and women didn't just "travel around" They usually stayed in one place in a home.

Brianna had tears in her eyes and said "I would go with you if you were planning to settle down and make a home, but I just can't do it if you plan to travel around through wilderness."

With sadness I said "I understand Brianna. You have different needs than me. I love you but I can't stay in one place right now. Maybe someday."

We held each other and both had tears in our eyes but we knew that our lives had different paths going forward.

The Psychic Soldier Series-Book 2-A Soldier is Born

Visiting America

After another month to make sure that my Samurai friends were ready to protect the Mission I was ready to take my leave.

Ramanda approached me and said "As your vassal I will be going with you to America."

I said "You really don't have to. I'm willing to give you your freedom to stay here."

He said "I have nothing keeping me here and I promised my loyalty to you. So if you are willing I will accompany you."

I thought about it and said "Okay—that sounds good. It will be great to have you with me and we can explore America together."

We left the next day to hike back south to Yokahama. It took a couple weeks to get there. When we did we checked into a Western inn to find beds and food.

We asked around and found out that the most Pacific crossings to America could be found in Hong Kong.

We booked passage there and got there in another week.

In Hong Kong we asked around the harbor and found out that most ships to America went around the tip of South America to the East Coast.

We wanted to go to San Francisco where passage was harder to find.

Finally, I was told we should look for Whalers which often docked there. The Whalers were from New England but sometimes went to the west coast of the United States looking for whales.

The Psychic Soldier Series-Book 2-A Soldier is Born

It took a couple of weeks of waiting, but we found a Whaler going to San Francisco to hunt for whales near there and because the Captain had a girlfriend who lived in the city.

The distance we would cross was vast and I was told that the crossing would could take a few months with stops on some islands in between.

We took passage and enjoyed most of the trip. I even got to go out on some of the whaling boats with the sailors.

However, after a few weeks we ran into a Hurricane which I they call Cyclones in those latitudes.

The Captain was a competent sailor and the boat was strong so we kept going to get through the storm to safer waters.

During the first day of the storm I was sick to death. I threw up everything I had eaten that day and was feeling green. Started looking for a way to not feel sick anymore.

Decided to go into a deep meditative state and then I was calm enough to not feel sick with all the boat swaying.

Gave myself mental commands to stay calm and relaxed. As I did that my ability to keep from being seasick improved dramatically.

After the meditation I was able to go on deck and hold the safety ropes to see what was going on. The sailors were amazed I wasn't in bed sick and they became very friendly showing me how the ship was battened down and facing the waves to avoid the worst of the storm.

I checked Ramanda and he looked a little green but kept his stoic and quiet personality even in the midst of the Cyclone. What a solid person he is I thought.

The next day we had passed through the storm and it was a real relief to everyone to see calm seas again.

After a month and half of voyaging we reached the Big Island of Hawaii.

Hawaii at that time was an independent kingdom where Americans and some Asians lived.

Europeans and Americans had only settled in Hawaii in the last few decades.

Sugarcane was a growing crop with an American being the main investor.

We went to the western side of the Big Island where most of the ships were anchored in an area which was not settled then but now has the modern city of Kailua-Kona in that location.

We found out that there was lots of trade with the Americas and ships were leaving for the West Coast of the United States every few days.

This led me to think about an opportunity to explore the island.

Ramanda was interested too and said "Let's look around and see what we find."

We said goodbye to the crew of the Whaler and thanked them for taking care of us and showing us an interesting time.

I was particularly interested in the Volcanos and had been told the tallest ones were climbable. Having climbed into the Himalayas these Volcanos didn't' worry me.

Looking for a native guide to the island I found a young man in the Harbor who agreed to guide us and even climb the Volcanos with for a modest fee. I was told it was probably a year's wages for him or he might not even see money most of the time.

We also rented horses to get around the Island faster and packaged supplies for camping and food to use along the way.

As we headed inland I learned from the native guide that he was a warrior and a member of the Royal Household of King Kamehameha. His name was Alika which meant "The Life" in Hawaiian.

He told us about the military training his people went through when they joined the Hawaiian military. Ramanda and I looked at each other since we wanted to learn more.

Even though the Hawaiians didn't have a powerful military force it looked from what Alika showed us that they had some intriguing acrobatic fighting moves.

First though we wanted to see the Big Island and climb the dormant Volcano Mauna Kea. It took us several days heading inland as the elevation climbed to get to the base of the mountain.

The climate changed too from tropical near the ocean to a more temperate and colder climate next to the mountain.

I estimated that the base of this volcano was already at about five thousand feet.

The climb was grueling because there were not any good trails. We followed rocks and old stream beds to get about halfway up the mountain in one day.

We decided to camp on the slopes where we found a flat area to pitch our tent next to a big boulder.

I could look out from there and see the outline of the Island with the shorelines in the distance.

We continued the next day to reach the crater where there was Snow! We walked around in the snow and had a snowball fight.

Imagine snow at the top of the Volcano while it was hot and sunny near the Ocean. It was quite a contrast.

*****

The next day we hiked down Mauna Kea and a few days later found ourselves at a government outpost on the northwest part of the Island. It was in a valley called Waippo valley which had some wild horses.

It was there that we met other members of the Hawaiian military and saw them training.

These soldiers were the modern inheritors of what were known as the ancient "Koa" warriors.

They were drilling in some of the ancient techniques which included strangulation cords and trip weapons.

We also saw them throwing volcanic rocks from high speed slings.

I tried sparring with one of the Koa warriors and he caught me in his strangulation cord time after time. I wasn't using my intuition but his skills were excellent and I couldn't avoid him getting me in a strangle hold with his cord. A very innovative form of fighting.

The next time the warrior caught me around the neck I managed to flip myself onto my feet and got my hand under the cord, then I twisted in a way he didn't expect and pulled it over my head.

The warrior was shocked because he said nobody had ever gotten out of the cord when he had already twisted it around someone's neck.

Ramanda and I spent a couple of days with the warriors learning more about their fighting techniques and weapons then left their village to go back to the western coast.

*****

On the coast we caught a paddle wheel trading ship heading to San Francisco. It was a modern ship and I got the engineer to give me an explanation of how the engine and paddle wheel worked.

It used coal to fuel a boiler which provided the steam pressure to move paddle wheels.

I learned that steamers like this one we normally only on the eastern coast of the United States but this one had headed around Cape Horn on the South end of South America to trade and bring passengers to San Francisco.

The stop in Hawaii was to pick up Sugar Cane to trade in San Francisco.

These people all had gold fever and planned to get rich from the gold in the California Mountains.

The Gold Rush

It took us another week to get to San Francisco. The sea was pretty calm and we only had one minor rain storm.

The year was 1848 and it was the beginning of the California gold rush.

Ramanda and I had heard about the Gold Rush news as far away as Yokahama, but arriving in the San Francisco Harbor was unbelievable.

The harbor was jammed with many ships from the Eastern United States and with ships from all over the world.

As we got ashore the docks were full of supplies coming in from all over the world. The supplies included shovels, picks, and all sorts of camping supplies, food, liquor, and much more.

Ramanda and I had chatted and decided to give gold mining a shot to see if we could earn money that way. We also just wanted to see the gold fields for ourselves.

I purchased the supplies we needed with my gold coins but the prices were high and I was almost out of money.

The supplies included pack horses, digging shovels, pans, and general camping supplies.

After a week of getting supplies and getting oriented we left San Francisco to get to the Sierra Nevada's.

We headed on the road east with thousands of others into the mountains above Sacramento. Many took the Sacramento River but we wanted to walk and learn the land surrounding us.

The trip took a couple of weeks on the trails which paralleled the Sacramento River Delta and we had many potential miners on the trail with us. We talked to them to learn more about gold mining and the general news of the area.

There were people from all over the world so a former British Soldier and a Japanese Samurai were not too out of place.

There wasn't much in the way of law and order so we had to watch out carefully for robbers who often stopped people on the trails to hold them up.

This happened to us but the gang was surprised with the result. It was after we had already been climbing up into the mountains for over a week.

We were just coming around the bend of a trail in a forest of Redwoods—which were some of the biggest trees I had ever seen. Suddenly we were confronted with three gang members who were holding their six shooters aimed at us about ten feet away.

One was tall and the other two were shorter but heavy. They all looked mean and had scars on their faces. We were sure they knew how to use their guns.

I had been so focused on looking at the trees I had not been using my intuition for seeing trouble at all.

Both Ramanda and I realized they had the drop on us and we would have to move carefully to gain control of the situation.

They ordered us to put down our pistols which we did and then ordered us to sit on the ground next to trees.

They basically tied us up around the trees and took our horses with all of our equipment. Then they searched our pockets and smiled when they got my remaining gold coins.

They left Ramanda with a small knife in his belt but took his Katana.

We looked down at the ground to avoid our captor's eyes and too look completely subservient.

Soon, they smiled and took off up with trail with our horses saying "Goodbye you stupid foreigners!"

I got us untied in about thirty minutes using a hidden knife and we took off running after them.

Ramanda and I were used to running and could go an entire day so we soon gained on their trail.

It was getting towards evening so we expected them to stop and camp somewhere not too far from the trail.

We also expected them to be careless because we looked harmless and they had all of our weapons.

They obviously didn't expect us to catch up with them being on our horses.

We followed the footprints of our horses which were distinctive. My horse had a right rear shoe which had a bent nail in it and was easy to see in footprints as a slash across the imprint.

The shoe imprints left the trail and went through a forest where they were harder to follow. So we looked for broken branches and leaves which had been disturbed in the lower brush.

It was getting towards evening so we looked for their campsite. We slowed down checking their trail for signs of their camp in the woods.

We came to a small stream with some flat ground next to it and sure enough they were drinking and laughing. They were talking about how stupid those foreigners were.

Ramanda and I decided to make our attack as easy as possible since we were tired from running all day.

We also made some choking ropes from available plants while we waited. Then relaxed late into the evening until they were all asleep next to their campfire.

We went around the campsite to the other side so the horses wouldn't take warning since they were picketed on the side near us.

We snuck into their camp and grabbed their weapons. It was easy for us because we both knew how to walk quietly through forests at night. Then we decided to teach them a lesson.

I threw a six gun cartridge into the fire to wake them up. It blew up and made a large noise while we both held our weapons on them.

They woke up and jumped when they saw us. One said "How the hell did you catch us. We should have been a day ahead of you on the horses?" We just smiled.

The tall one said "You don't want to make an issue with us you stupid foreigners. Just leave now."

The other two were looking for a chance to jump us.

Then they all rushed us which was a big mistake. We could have shot them but really want to teach them a lesson-not kill them.

The two heavy ones tried to knock me down and beat on me. Instead I pivoted around, kicked them both in the knees to get them on the ground then put our choking ropes around both of their necks.

Ramanda used his knife to cut the belt off the tall guy and then put it under his neck.

They were all bleary eyed and yelled for us to give them mercy.

I said "Well, you didn't try to kill us so we won't kill you. But we are going to make you sorry you attacked us and took our stuff."

They looked scared. Thinking about a proper punishment I finally had a lightbulb and smiled.

I whispered to Ramanda and he smiled. We tied them up well and started our plan.

I whittled a brand out of wood and stuck it in the fire. It said "THIEF". When it was hot enough we held down each man and held the heated and burning wood to their foreheads until it burned the word into them. You could smell the skin burning.

They first one screamed and cursed us royally. The ones waiting and looked really upset. They were sweating too. We branded all three.

Then we took everything back including their boots and left them tied up in the campsite.

We headed the horses out into the night and looked for a campsite several miles away which we could protect.

Each of us took turns as a guard but we didn't see anything except some deer and raccoons.

*****

The rest of the trip to the mining towns was pretty boring but we did hear a lot of travelers laughing about the gang members who had their heads branded with the word "THIEF".

We finally got to the mountain mining town of Soldiers Gulf which was later renamed to the name of Volcano Town.

The area was crowded with thousands of miners in tents. In fact it was a tent city with several hundred tents with a main street full of tents which were gradually being replaced with wood buildings.

Ramanda and I went to the nearest bar to find out where we could stay and how to get food.

We were told we could pitch our tents on the outskirts of town at no cost.

Food was going to cost a lot though—as well as almost all other supplies which had to be packaged in from San Francisco.

We also asked about mining claims and were told we could see a map at the Assay Office and look for gold wherever there were no claims.

We pitched our tent in an open area and went to buy some food at a restaurant/bar.

As the evening got later there were several fights at surrounding bars which nobody broke up—because there was no Sherriff to keep the peace.

Finally we heard some gunfire. One of the drunk miners stumbled out of his bar holding his stomach. Everyone gathered round as he bled out and died.

Then another drunk miner game out of the bar. He spit on the dead man and said "I told him I got his claim legally and he didn't listen. So I shot him." Then he gave another mean spit to the body and walked out of town back to his tent. Nobody stopped him.

We asked around and were told his name was Sam Twist and he was a miner and gunfighter with a mean temper. If he challenged you-you better back down quick or you would be dead.

*****

The next morning Ramanda and I set out with plans to look for some gold.

We had to hike ten miles through the woods to find unused spots to prospect. This was after passing on several locations which already had miners on them.

Walking way up the stream locally known as Indian Way we finally found an area where there were no other miners.

We started panning. To do panning you dig some sand or dirt, then swirl water around your plan to get rid of the lighter dirt of sand. Then you look for little shiny sparkles in the bottom of the plan. You then judge the site by how many sparkling metal flakes you have.

We only found slight trace flakes of gold. Nothing worth real effort.

Spending about eight hours digging and crouching we were pretty tired when we quit and went back to our tent. After a couple of weeks of this tiring process we were almost ready to quit.

The Psychic Soldier Series-Book 2-A Soldier is Born

I wondered if I could use my intuition to find us some gold. I went into a meditation one morning and kept thinking about where I could find some unexploited gold.

I finally got an image to look for a glade near a stream with a small pool surrounded by rocks.

Told Ramanda about my dream and he knew enough about me by then to trust my intuition.

Next day we started searching up the Indian Way to look for this location.

Camped out up there and went at least thirty miles up the stream before we gave up.

Next day coming back down the stream we saw a side stream. I said lets give it a try. So Ramanda nodded and we went a mile up the stream.

Sure enough we found the location from my dream. Nothing was disturbed so we knew nobody had tried to pan there recently.

Our first pan showed five gold flecks. We panned in a circle and found a direction with up to twenty flecks to a pan. As we moved in that direction up the hillside I actually got a pan with a small gold nugget.

Ramanda and I were smiling and we decided to quit at that time.

We packed up and noted landmarks to register our claim.

Back in town at the Assay office that evening we registered our claim. The Assayer wanted some evidence that it was a real claim so we showed him our flakes and the gold nugget.

He held the nugget and said "Very nice. I can see this has come from a good claim. Probably a rich vein nearby."

We tried to keep it quiet, but word got around town and other miners wanted to toast us in the nearest bar.

It was a nice party that night with lots of back slapping but we went back to our tent early so as not to get too drunk to be taken advantage of.

*****

Over the next few weeks Ramanda and I took out more gold which we turned in at the Assay office and started to build a nice little nest egg.

We also had to do some deceptive tracking since people started trying to follow us to our claim.

Ramanda and I were trying to decide how long to stay in town since just becoming rich goldminers wasn't really why we were there.

After a couple of months I was in a bar one night after it was too dark to mine when a drunken Sam Twist came up to us trying to be friendly.

I said thanks and offered him a drink. He gave me an insincere smile and sat down.

As we talked he kept bringing up how nice a claim we had and that his claim was running out.

Finally he suggested he join us as a partner. We said thanks but we were fine with things as they were.

Then he got mad and said "So I'm not good enough for you?"

I tried to calm him by saying "There is no problem. We think you are fine. We just don't want any other partners."

This didn't go any good and he got angrier and said "You think you are better than me. Huh?"

I could tell this wasn't going anywhere good so we got up to leave. He yelled "Sit down here and finish your drinks."

I'd had enough and said "Leave us alone or you will regret it."

This caused Sam to bring out a murderous look and the other bar patrons left in a hurry or backed up against an opposite wall.

I knew that Sam was about to draw on me so I quickly used my intuition to see where he would shoot.

I felt he was going to shoot me straight on in the gut so when I saw him tighten his grip on the gun and that we was about to shoot I dived left.

His gun went off aiming to where I had been and mine went off as I dived while aiming at his heart.

He was faster than me but shot in the wrong direction.

My bullet hit true and he dropped onto his back with a look of pure amazement. My bullet had hit him square in the heart. Then he was dead.

The other people in the bar surrounded his body then I heard some cheers "Damn he killed him!" Another said "Wow-- Sam got what he deserved". A woman stood over the body and spit "That bastard hurt me and I'm glad he's dead."

Pretty soon everyone was patting me on the back on offering to buy me drinks. I wasn't happy at all about the confrontation. We just wanted to mine our gold and leave town.

Later than night I staggered back to my tent with Ramanda holding me and guiding me the right way. I fell into my bed in a stupor and woke with a big hangover. Ouch.

*****

We went back to our claim to work it the next day and the week rolled on pretty much the same.

On Saturday evening we were taking a break at our favorite bar "The Happy Miner" when several leading men of the town came over to us. This included the owners of the larger stores and several bars and restaurants. Even the local church minister was part of the group.

They were smiling and all said hello then asked me to meet them in private.

I didn't sense any danger but told them I wanted my man Ramanda to wait outside the room for me. They all understood and agreed.

We went to one of the few wooden buildings in town and all sat at a table with chairs which had been laid out. The front and back doors were closed and locked.

They were all giving me this funny smile and looked nervous. I didn't know what to expect.

I said "So what is it that you have all dragged me down here for?"

They were looking at each other when the minister spoke up "We have been mighty impressed with the way you handle yourself in town. Were you ever in the army?"

My ears perked up and I said "Well yes, in India I was in the British Army and we fought several battles."

Several of the men nodded their heads and one said "I thought so."

Then the minister continued "You can see this is a pretty lawless town and we have lots of killings and shootings……" as his voice trailed off.

I had never been in this part of the world so I didn't get the drift of what he was talking about.

Finally, one of the other store keepers said "I can see you're confused—let me be clear—We all want you to be our Sherriff."

You could have knocked me over with a feather. I really didn't expect that.

I replied "Uhhh.. that is really nice of you. But I'm a miner, not a Sherriff. I also don't think I'm the right person to be Sherriff for you."

Another store owner chimed in "Yes, we know you have a good claim and a partner. Can't your partner work the claim while you are Sherriff? We can also help find you workers which can be trusted to work your claim."

"But we need your skills to help make this town a safe place for everyone. The fact that you don't want to be Sherriff is another reason we want you."

I took some time to think about it. Everyone could see me thinking. Then I said "I'll give it a try to help clean up your town. But I'm not sure how long I will stay."

They all looked relieved and the minister said "We knew you would do it. You are an answer to our prayers."

I also told them. "I will also need an office with a jail to do this job". They mentioned that one was already being built and was nearly finished."

The minister had one last question "We still need to settle what to pay you. What do you want?"

I smiled and said "Well, my mine is doing pretty well so I don't need any money right now. What I would really like it that when the town is stable you all agree that when I want to leave you will not try to hold me."

They seemed a little stunned but all agreed that if I made the city safe they would give me a going away party.

So I began my unexpected job of Sherriff for the next couple of years.

Volcano Town Sherriff

Went out and hired some workers to help in my eyes around the town and give me the news in a hurry wherever I was.

Had to see the local blacksmith to have him make me a Sherriff's star since one didn't exist in the town.

I started doing patrols that evening when the miners were at the bars and getting rowdy.

The first bar I entered everyone looked at me with a wary eye and made space at the bar when I walked up to it.

I only had some Sasporilla since I really didn't want to drink on the job to keep my reflexes sharp.

My plan was to circulate around the bars as the evening went on to see what was going on.

About ten o'clock somebody ran into the bar to tell me there was a problem down the street.

I ran down the street and saw a fight going on between four or five drunken miners.

Told them to stop or I would lock them all up. They kept fighting and I could see knives or guns would come out soon.

Wading into the fray I hit people with a stick I was carrying to knock them to the ground or break them up from fighting.

Then I yelled for them to stop fighting and shut up. Took out my gun, got behind them and steered them all to the jail.

Good thing the jail was large enough to fit them all. I locked them all in for the night and gave them a lecture that they would be locked up longer if they got drunk and fought again.

Then I went back on Patrol and locked up a couple more fighting drunks for the night.

Told the hungover group in the morning that each time they got arrested for drunken fighting they would be locked up for an additional night.

Drunken fighting took a nosedive after I started locking people up for public drunkenness.

My first real challenge happened a couple of weeks later when a group of six miners from the Wilder family came into town to blow off steam after a particularly good week mining.

The Wilders were all known as tough former gang members and thieves who had no morals or ethics. A pretty tough group. Most people believed they had stolen their mine and killed the original owners—but nobody could prove it.

They all went to Fat Als Saloon to drink and play cards. I kept on my rounds and made one round there where the Wilders and others were all pretty peaceful and having fun.

I came back a couple of hours later when the Wilders were drunk and saw they were picking on a young man who was obviously brand new to bars and our wild town.

They were spinning him around and forcing him to drink.

They were also abusing the whores who were yelling and trying to get away from them.

I walked up to them and told them "That's it. Stop right now or you are all going to jail."

They thought they were tough and pulled out their pistols. Four pistols against one-with two more angry men, and they were surrounding me. Everyone else rapidly cleared out of the bar.

This could be real a challenge.

One shot his pistol at me but I knew a second beforehand he would do so and twisted around to get ahold of his neck with a choke hold while hit bullet hit the floor.

Then I put out some Kung Fu kicks to put several others on the floor.

Finally, the biggest and baddest of them aimed his gun at me to shoot.

I knew he was going to do that and could have avoided it but used my couple of seconds of foresight to shoot him in the heart.

So when he gun came around to aim at me he was already dying. My bullet had caught him in the gut.

Within thirty seconds five of the gang were on the floor, the worst one was dead, and the youngest was standing there white as a sheet.

They had all gone from being in control to being under my control and looking scared instead of overbearing. I got them all up and moved at gunpoint to the jail.

Everyone else watching was also in shock. They expected me to be dead by this time.

After that when people saw me they were definitely frightened of causing trouble.

*****

There were a few women in town including the daughter of the minister.

She was dark haired and was tall with a pretty solid frame for a girl.

Her name was Wanda. I got to know her after being invited for dinner to their place by her father.

We would go on walks, have picnics near the streams, and she became a good friend.

Again, I still thought of myself as young so didn't want to settle down. We just had a casual romance but were careful since she was a darling of the town's and I didn't want to get her into trouble.

The townspeople noticed us together and smiled when we went by. I guess my relationship with Wanda made me look more human in their eyes. The townspeople also hoped I might marry her and stay in town as their Sherriff.

*****

One of the biggest criminals known in the mountains was Terry the Hatchet. He was reputed to not only be one of the fastest guns, but also known to throw a deadly hatchet to kill some of his opponents.

He usually worked mining towns further south, but I think he had heard about me and wanted to challenge me when he came to Volcano town.

So one night I'm doing my rounds when I came into the Bear Bar and saw one man standing at the bar with everyone else at least ten feet away.

He was a large but muscular man with long hair that looked very greasy. He had a long scar on his right cheek and his arms were covered in scars. So I knew he was also an experienced knife fighter.

I asked a few people who he was and they said "He is deadly. He is known as "Terry the Hatchet" and is known to have killed many people and Sheriffs in other mining towns.

Terry was drinking whiskey at the bar and looked generally angry. He saw me and turned to talk with me.

I figured he wanted to have a confrontation anyway so I might as well oblige.

Holding out his hand he said "Let's shake hands Sherriff. I always like to meet the big cheese in each town." He gave a dirty and greasy smile and I could smell his bad breath.

I shook his hand and said "I've heard about your reputation, and let me just give you fair warning. I'm not a pushover. As long as you don't hurt anyone in this town you can stay here"

He smiled and said "I will enjoy a few days here before we get down to it."

I left him then to finish my rounds and everyone else was wondering when the blowup would happen.

Terry was at the bars at night and went out to look at claims during the day.

It was the third day when several prospectors met me at the jail. One said "We just found a rich claim and were going to file at the Assessors when that nasty Terry came up to us and said we had to sell him the mine or we would all have deadly accidents. What could we do but fork over our claim to stay alive?"

The Psychic Soldier Series-Book 2-A Soldier is Born

I said "Do you have witnesses?" Sure they said. Several people near the Assessor's office saw our argument.

As Sherriff I had also followed him at night with my invisibility shield on and saw him casing the local banks too.

It was time to deal with Terry the Hatchet. Normally I don't like to kill people when they are thru and thru wrecked as a useful person to society—then there is nothing else to do but kill them.

Went to his favorite Bear Bar that evening to have it out. He saw me coming and straightened up at the bar.

He wasn't drinking anything but water. I said "Terry, you are under arrest for stealing miner's claims. Come with me quietly so we don't have a scene."

"You don't want a scene?" he smiled "Then drop your badge on the floor and leave. I don't need to kill you."

I took a stance which showed everyone I wasn't going to back down. Everyone ran to the other side of the room or out of the door.

We both stood there for a minute staring at each other. Then I got a quick intuition he was about to fire.

I had been practicing my draw so I drew and fired. Then I jumped to the side of where I knew his bullet would go.

He fired and it hit empty air. But my bullet hit him in the left chest. While he still had some strength he threw his axe at me. I knew it was coming and put up my arm to deflect it with my long knife.

Then I went to stand over him since he was prostrate and since I'd shot him in the face. It had to be done. He was dangerous to everyone around him.

Everyone in town was in awe of me. There was no trouble at all when I did my rounds and if someone was starting something and saw me they would take off running.

*****

Most people were just scared of me. It was time for me to leave town. I had money and I was bored being Sherriff.

But I didn't want to leave the town in danger so I decided to train some deputies.

I looked for former military men who were fed up with prospecting. Found several.

After I found out they were interested we did training. This included with firearms and in fighting to subdue violent people.

Over the next couple of months we practiced and I taught them a lot. Lots of practice on firing and with different scenarios.

Also had fighting classes where I taught them martial arts.

Then I made the leaders of the town aware I was leaving and suggested they form a core group who could assist the new Deputies and whomever they elected as Sherriff.

The leaders accepted this as a good solution with me leaving town.

Then I sold the gold claim to some of these same leaders and had the sales price and many gold coins taken to a bank in San Francisco.

I would take some coins with me secreted in multiple places in my clothes and horse with drafts available for the rest of my money back to the Wells Fargo Bank in San Francisco.

Ramanda and I had a party in one of the bars where many of the townsfolk wished us goodbye. The leaders who had hired me were grateful and told me they owed me if I ever came back.

But, I think many were glad to see us go because they considered me too dangerous to have around.

Indian Country

Stories were told in the bars of men who had met the Indians out west and surprisingly, not all were horror stories.

These were tribes of people who lived all over the country. There were apparently many different cultures with different ways.

Being foreigners in America Ramanda and I were not raised with the prejudice most Americans held for the Indians.

Based on some advice from travelers in Volcano town we thought the Utes were pretty peaceful and might be a good group of Indians to meet.

Ramanda and I set off the next day after the party to cross the Sierra Nevada Mountains east of us.

It was getting on to winter and we didn't want to end up like the Donner party who spent the winter in the mountains near Truckee and resorted to Cannibalism before they were rescued.

No-we took some fast horses and all the supplies we could pack including snowshoes.

We crossed in November before the snow got too deep. Even so we saw some majestic peaks as our five horses made trail going east.

Three of the horses were just pack horses and the other two were for Ramanda and me to ride.

My time in the Himalayas had helped too, so the altitude was easy for me and I knew how to make a snow cave to sleep in if I had to.

Ramanda was always stoic and never complained so I made sure he had the right clothes and equipment for the mountains to keep up with me.

We proceeded for several days as the mountains got higher and then we ran into snowy weather.

The snow wasn't too deep but the temperatures dropped to zero degrees Fahrenheit at night. I could sense that a big storm was coming.

I dug us a snow tunnel with Ramanda's help. We dug into a drift under some trees. It took both of us several hours. Finally we had a small tunnel which one person could use to get into.

Then I crawled into the tunnel and dug into the ceiling as well as widening the room so we could both fit into it.

The finishing effort was to cover the floor with spruce branches. This would protect us from body heat leaking through to the now underneath, and would provide some insulation for us in our blankets.

We made a cooking fire in a wind sheltered area near our snow shelter and cooked some meat for dinner.

Since the campfire was built on top of the snow, it kept sinking into the snow until the bed of burnt wood under the first logs kept it from sinking anymore.

Water for some soup was melted from the snow.

Then we hobbled the horses nearby in a protected area in the trees and tied some blankets on our horses to help them stay warm too—even though they could take some pretty cold weather.

The temperature kept dropping and the moon had circles around it which confirmed a storm was coming.

Finally we moved our blankets and other supplies into the snow shelter and closed up the snow tunnel to retain heat. A couple of candles gave us some light.

We wrapped up in our blankets and squirmed into the branches. Between the snow insulation, the branches, and our blankets we were nice and warm.

There were even drips on the ceiling of our shelter showing that the air temperature was actually above freezing.

We slept nice and comfy while we could hear the wind howling outside blowing.

*****

In the morning it was dark so I lit the candles again. Had to dig extra snow out of the tunnel since it was buried outside.

Then we put on all our clothes and crawled out of the snow cave to take a look.

The storm was still going on with a high wind. Everything was covered with drifts. I checked the horses, fed and watered them and made sure they were protected from the winds.

We had to stay there and wait until the storm played out.

Collected more dead branches from up in the trees since the ground was all covered with snow.

We both worked on setting up more branches and rocks to protect our fire from the wind then cooked more to eat and stay warm.

We ate some smoked fish and had some hot coffee along with some hard bread.

Staying outside in the wind for a while the wind was strong and we were getting cold so we went back into the shelter.

A few more hours digging more space for ourselves, then we made a small fire inside with a hole in the roof on the side to make more coffee.

It was nice to have a rest day so we talked a lot about what it would be like to meet the Indians.

The next day the storm was over. We got out of the shelter and saw that a lot of snow had fallen and that everything was covered even deeper.

Fortunately, most of it was in drifts with shallow snow in between so we could ride our horses around the drifts—and struggled over a few of them.

The next couple of days the trail descended into the eastern side of the Sierras. We came down out of the high mountains to Lake Tahoe where we stayed a couple of days.

Here we met the Washoe Indian tribe. We came upon their village near the shores to Lake Tahoe and had already brought trade goods to keep them happy.

Using sign language we offered them beads, glass, knives, and a few guns as their braves came up to us on the trail.

The Indians were friendly and offered for us to stay with them while the weather was difficult for traveling.

We took them up on their offer and gradually learned the Washoe language as well as sign language to communicate with other tribes we would meet.

After staying for several weeks we decided to push on during a warm spell. The Washoe's gave us friendly goodbyes and wished us well our way.

*****

Descending further we came to what was called "Truckee Meadows" which was lightly settled and also on the main east west trail to California.

We headed east towards Utah and the City of Salt Lake. This area had been settled a few years ago and we were excited about seeing civilization again.

Another couple of weeks took us to Salt Lake through some really dry areas. We had to carry lots of extra bags of water to have enough to drink on some days.

In the town of Mormons we found it very comfortable and peaceful, but the residents didn't really mix with non Mormons and foreigners.

There were no real bars in town but we did find a couple of places where non Mormons congregated.

In one of these restaurants and Inns I talked with many other travelers from all over the country.

I heard about the vicious tribe of Indians called the "Comanches".

The Psychic Soldier Series-Book 2-A Soldier is Born

They were so tough they had stopped the Mexicans from settling east from Mexico, and the Americans from settling west. They had held off both sides for fifty years.

My curiosity was high even though everyone warned me to not go anywhere near their lands. They told us "It would be certain death and probably from horrible torture."

However, I was determined to learn how they could be such tough warriors without the guns the Mexicans or Americans had. Knew it would be dangerous but if they were that good fighters I wanted to learn how they did it. My goal was to become the best and most dangerous fighter in the world.

The Comanches

The journey from Salt Lake City, in the Utah Territories would take a couple of months.

I also had to contend with it being winter so travel in places might be difficult.

It was about a six hundred mile trip and we would need to skirt the southern part of the Rockies to get to Comanche Territory.

I had heard if you showed them you were a great warrior they might accept you.

Ramanda and I bought trade goods and enough supplies for a month. After that we would have to live off the land.

We headed south east thru what is now modern day Colorado and New Mexico to where Texas is today.

It took us many weeks. We ran into the Navajos who were a friendly agrarian people who farmed and grew crops.

Sitting around some campfires at their mud bricked homes we heard many tales about how the Indians all came from inside the Earth and came out into the world again after some ancient great calamities. The Navajos didn't know the details but said the Hopi Indians were the keepers of the ancient knowledge.

Might be worth visiting here in the future.

Heading further east we came to the Old Spanish City of Santa Fe. This city had been founded by the Spanish back in the seventeenth century and was a combination of old pueblos and Spanish architecture. It was still part of Mexico when I first arrived there.

The Psychic Soldier Series-Book 2-A Soldier is Born

Ramanda and I decided to rest there a week or two and we spent a lot of time in the local Cantinas.

Meeting some traders and local Indians I asked more questions about the Comanches.

I got an earful-most of which was to stay away and not get myself killed unnecessarily. But I did learn that some groups of Spanish and Indians did trade with them.

I convinced one of these groups to include us in their next trade meeting. We paid them and offered our fighting escort services on the way.

The meeting was setup to be in a mountain valley a week's travel northeast of San Fe.

It was way up in the mountains – just below where the snow got heavy.

We met in a valley which was protected from the winds next to a river which flowed all year round. This area was close to the western reaches of Comanche Territory.

The Comanche village was made of Tepees. It was the first real Tepee village I had seen.

Even more interesting was that the head Comanche traders were well dressed like Europeans. They spoke English well too. These were not just savages.

The trading started and what I had heard was true. They were not only trading regular goods, but white women and children they had captured.

You could tell these women had been badly abused. They looked sick, thin, and several were pregnant.

I communicated with the Comanche Traders to see if they would take us with them in their travels. That we were great warriors. They laughed at this until we offered to fight their braves for their agreement.

They agreed and both Ramanda and I found ourselves in a circle with just our knives, facing some young braves with their knives.

The entire tribe and our trading group were gathered around.

We asked how would we decide who won?

The chief Comanche trader laughed and said "You will fight them until one side is dead. If you die, then you will not be joining us. If you win you will replace these braves and travel with us.

I thought that was pretty harsh but had to do my best at this point.

*****

I started circling with the tallest and strongest brave. Ramanda was with the older one.

We were both feeling out each other's fighting skills.

This brave was about my age and had several scars on his body so he must be experienced.

He charged me and yelled. He was fast as a snake and almost hit me with his knife.

But my intuition came in handy as usual and I sidestepped and slashed him with my knife in the side.

He was bleeding but this hardly slowed him down. He twirled and actually drew blood from me with a cut on my right arm.

I was really surprised because I hadn't been cut by anyone since my tussle with the Blue Bear in the Himalayas.

Turning around again I went low and slashed at his leg when I knew he would be in the right position.

He went down on this face. I jumped on his back and quickly had the knife on the side of his neck with him in a chokehold.

I looked at the trading Chief to see if he still wanted me to kill the brave. The Chief was quiet but I could tell he was very upset.

Didn't know it yet but the brave was his eldest son. The Chief told me to get off him. That I had won.

I did so and saw Ramanda had already dispatched the other brave.

The young man I had almost killed gave me an evil look. I knew he was looking for revenge, and the Indians carried their grudges closely.

*****

We left with the tribe in another week after trading was done. The others traders we had come with headed back to the safety of Santa Fe.

I was told we were heading back south into their main tribal areas. This was just one band of Comanche's and we might run into others on the trail. They were not all friendly with each other.

When we stopped at night to camp the Braves wanted to try themselves with me and Ramanda. We looked forward to these challenges because they helped to sharpen our fighting skills.

These braves were real knife fighters. We practiced with real knives where the winner achieved a streak of broken skin on the opponent.

I consciously tried to not use my intuition to focus just on my knife fighting skills.

Found out I could do with a lot of improvement as I ended up these matches with lots of streaks.

One young brave who was about eighteen years old was fast as a snake.

He kept getting the better of me until I learned to thrust and move my knife as fast as he did. This took me a lot of matches over several weeks.

Ramanda was already a master with his Katana so didn't need to learn anything new—except how to fight opponents who used shorter blades.

******

As we were traveling word came of treachery from the white government on the Comanche's.

A large group of whites had tried to capture thirty three Comanche Chiefs to force them to release all their white prisoners. The Chiefs got away.

Our Comanche leaders met with other Chiefs in the middle of Comanche territory. The Comanche's were planning some large raids in retaliation.

Our own group of Comanches were joining the raid and we had to go along. I had decided I would try to warn the settlers along the way.

We stopped the first evening to camp and the braves were all painting themselves up with war paint.

As we traveled southeast the Comanches would attack individual ranches and other travelers met on the way. I stayed out of the way to stay in the tribes good graces.

After a couple of weeks the Chief told everyone we would be attacking a couple of towns with other Comanche groups. About four hundred fighters overall.

The Chief asked me if we planned to go. I said "Yes but we don't want to fight other whites." The Chief accepted that response.

So we traveled on our horses to the town of Victoria in what is now Southeast Texas. The townspeople had been warned Comanches were coming and were ready for us. They knew they had to fight and would be killed or captured if they didn't.

The Indians entered the town to loot and pillage and were driven back by lots of rifle fire from the buildings.

I was already out of the way of the main fighting outside the town so I turned invisible and headed into town.

Found a good sniper location and started firing on the Comanches with my rifle.

Between my shooting accuracy and my intuition of their movements I started taking down Indians with each shoot.

I saw the Chiefs signaling each other and they soon backed out of town to regroup. They thought it was just the townspeople who were shooting them.

Then they attacked again and more braves were shot out of their saddles.

Some of these shots were mine. When the Indians looked for the source of my shot they couldn't see me or my rifle since we were both invisible.

After a second attempt on the town they regrouped outside the town and decided they had enough. The Comanches decided to head back west.

I quickly left my perch in town and sneaked back to my horse which Ramanda was holding outside of town.

We blended in with the tribe again on the way west.

The whole group was surprised because we were then blindsided by a group of Texas Rangers who had been following the Indians.

The Rangers opened up on the tribe with a real broadside of gunfire. The Comanches fought back of course but there was very little cover.

The fire kept coming as we kept retreating. I went invisible and warned Ramanda where to ride to miss the bullets so we made it through.

*****

We got away with eighty dead brave losses. These were a lot for the tribe to make up.

As we headed west some more families were attacked and some were captured. Those captured included young women and some men.

I couldn't stop the braves from killing some of the children although it made me really sick.

The Psychic Soldier Series-Book 2-A Soldier is Born

Wondered seriously if I had made a mistake riding with these Indians. The Comanches had an innate cruelty I'd never seen before they tortured and killed many victims and seemed pretty happy about it.

After a couple more weeks when we reached an area which was safe from white attacks, the Indians decided to have fun with their prisoners.

They staked out a couple of men and several women naked in the sun. The men had their eyelids cutoff so the sun would dry their eyes and they would go blind.

The women were raped by the braves until they were bloody. Then the women started burning the prisoners with burning stocks. The screaming was continuous until the prisoners went unconscious from the pain.

I had been watching disgusted and I didn't want to take on the whole tribe, but I couldn't take anymore. I wanted to free these people and talked to Ramanda who agreed with me that this was a very dishonorable thing these Indians were doing.

We decided to wait until evening to free the prisoners. There were over seventy Indians braves in the tribal camp so it might be the end of us.

But I couldn't stand the torture these captives were going through. We had to make a difference and get them out or die in the process.

*****

We waited until it was late at night when even the prisoners had stopped yelling and were trying to rest.

There were eight prisoners in the camp. Five staked out and three bound in a tent.

My plan was to get away when all the Indians were asleep although they had hair trigger wakefulness about sensing noise or problems in their camp.

Once we got the prisoners free I would try to get them to horses too.

Ramanda went to loosen some horses where they were staked, and to sneak into the tent and untie the prisoners. I went to the staked out prisoners to cut their bonds, and give them some clothes to put on as well as moccasins.

Told them all to keep quiet too. The men with their eyelids cutoff were blinded from the sun, but might recover given enough time.

I led them all holding a rope towards to horses, whispering to them all to keep quiet. I'm sure they were all in pain, but they were even more afraid of being recaptured so were very quiet.

We got to the horses when the Indians became aware of our escape.

Ten braves had woken and were running towards us and I could see it was going to be the fight of my life. The rest of the camp was still waking up and getting their weapons. They were carrying axes and some had bows and arrows.

I figured that the only way to stop these Indians was to really shock them and scare them. This would not be easy.

As the Indians came towards us I turned invisible and ran to kill them. They saw the escaped prisoners and as they did ran towards them to re-capture or kill them.

I didn't give them any chance at all, but started swinging my sword and knife through them all.

They got to within twenty feet of the prisoners who all started screaming, then I struck and all anyone could see was blood and guts flying while all ten of the braves hit the ground dead.

The captives stopped screaming in shock. I re-appeared and told them I would protect them. To get on the horses and get ready to go.

Ramanda came up with his prisoners from the Tepee chased by another twenty braves. He turned to fight the braves as the prisoners raced for the horses.

I ran up to provide him support. Ramanda was surrounded by Braves who were attacking him. He didn't have the invisibility capability to hide that I did.

Five Indians surrounded him. I was chopping my way towards him when he went down. They were cutting him, shooting him with arrows, and one was scalping him.

I got to his side and killed the Indians surrounding him but it was too late. My best friend was mortally wounded.

We had just a few seconds and he said to me "Tristan, this is a good death helping the prisoners. I've enjoyed my time as your servant and go to my death happily." Then he drew his final breath and died.

Other Indians were already racing towards me and the prisoners. I had to act fast.

I made a loud scream and yelled in the Comanche language "You are all dogs I challenge all of you to the death you cowards before you attack the prisoners again."

This stopped all of the braves to look towards me and then they moved to surround me.

I then declared "I am a god and will strike you all down if you don't leave now!"

Several arrows were released towards me. I avoided them all and turned invisible.

Hearing scared "Yeeehs" from the braves I headed towards the circle and started chopping. I was killing a brave every couple of seconds and the rest could see blood spurting and limbs being cut and heads rolling on the earth in a line which kept going.

After the fifth brave died, they finally panicked and took off at a run. They really did feel they were fighting a god and didn't want to die.

Then I quickly made sure all the prisoners were on their horses, with them all tied together, and we took off west.

We crossed a river and went upstream a couple of miles to cover our tracks, then found a good hiding place for the day.

Traveling mostly at night I took my charge to a settlement fifty miles to the west to get them medical help.

There I helped the townspeople bandage them and the lidless ones were given covers for their eyes, small ones for the day and larger ones to help them recover overall.

The prisoner women were taken charge of by the white women in the settlement to find a place to sleep and help them with their recoveries.

I had sworn all the prisoners to not say anything about my fighting or disappearing skills since it would seem too strange to the townspeople. The prisoners were grateful to me and gave me tearful thanks.

Instead what we told the townspeople was that the prisoners had made the escape themselves and I just helped them with the horses and road with them.

The townspeople were questioning how anyone could escape from the Comanches but they saw how the former prisoners were wounded and didn't question them any further.

I stayed in the town for a few days to get my energy back, think about my lost friend Ramanda, and plan what I would do next.

My thoughts took me back to the mysterious stories I had heard about the Hopis back in New Mexico about people who lived underground.

It seemed it was time to look them up.

Meeting the Hopis

I asked around and found out one of the Hopi tribes was peaceful and lived in an area north of Santa Fe close to the Navajos.

I still had my horse and Ramada's old horse to use for packing. After laying in some food and other supplies I took to the trail back towards Santa Fe.

Reaching Santa Fe in a few weeks I went into a Cantina to ask for directions to the Hopi reservation.

While I was asking around I found a middle aged Indian from the reservation who said he was in Santa Fe to trade and would be going back to the reservation soon.

His name was Cochito. He was thin with long hair and many wrinkles. We left town on a trip into the mountains going northwest.

One day we came to a valley in the desert with ruins of an amazing ancient Indian city. He told me it was called Chaco Canyon and there used to be thousands of Anastasi Indians who lived there hundreds of years ago.

The ruins were amazing and some were even several stories tall. We rested there that night and I dreamed of the city when it was vital and full of people. It was amazing to see all of those Indians living in their advanced city.

We left the next morning to head further west and north.

After another couple of weeks we came to more Indian villages. These villages used Adobe multi-level dwelling designs like I had seen back on the outskirts of Santa Fe.

The Psychic Soldier Series-Book 2-A Soldier is Born

Cochito told me this was his Hopi village. He was very friendly and let me stay in an empty dwelling. He also offered me to eat with his family. We had corn bread and some fruits for dinner.

The next day I met various members of the tribe including the elders and a medicine man.

Talk some about my travels and adventures around the world and they were very interested.

Finally, the medicine man offered me to attend one of their spiritual ceremonies in three nights at the time of the full moon.

I was looking forward to it. In the meantime I wandered around the village to learn how people thought and to just sit and think about my life.

Losing Ramanda was a big loss since he was a good companion and my only long term friend.

What did I really want out of my life?

*****

It was also during this time that I met a young woman named "Chepi" which meant fairy in their language. She was thin with beautiful features and very dark hair. I could imagine her as a fairy from Celtic lore.

I saw her carrying water one day and offered to help her. In turn she started teaching me the Hopi language one word at a time.

Over several days I learned quite a few words to help make myself understood.

*****

The night of the spiritual ceremony came and I was told by Cochito that it would be held in a Kiva. He showed me the Kiva. It was a sunken circular room with a wooden roof.

He said there were ten men who would be meeting in the Kiva. We would all enter naked. Then a fire would heat it up and we would sweat. This was when the ceremony would start.

That night we entered the Kiva as planned. We all sat cross legged on the floor.

The Hopis started chanting and I continued with them. After an hour we were all sweating freely and a drink was passed around. I didn't know it at the time but Peyote was lacing the drink to give us all an advanced state of consciousness.

After another half hour we all started having visions. Especially me since the drug was new to my system and I wasn't used to it.

Here was my vision:

> My vision was of a large canyon I seemed to be flying through. Then it narrowed to one side canyon and then to a cave in that canyon. I landed and walked into the cave.
>
> In the cave I met what I can only describe as wise elders. The elders smiled at me and took me deep in the cave.
>
> There were many machines in the cave and they told me that Indians used to live there.
>
> We entered another tunnel where we took some type of open railroad. This led to a huge open cavern full of buildings which seemed to touch the sky.

Then the vision faded…..

I woke all sweaty and wondering what had really happened.

The other shared their visions with the group which were mainly about animals like Hawks or Coyotes.

It came to be my turn and I told them about the city I had seen. They were very excited and the medicine man told me a story:

> *Long ago the story passed down through the ages was that our people came from below the Earth. That there was a great catastrophe which our ancestors avoided by living beneath the earth and that they came out to live in this world again. This was ages ago and before the great flood which the ancestors also lived through. You seem to have had a vision of this great underground world we came from. It is a wonderful blessing.*

My eyes were open wide from this story and I wanted to visit this lost inner earth location.

Over the next few days I spent more time with Chepi and had several talks with the Medicine man.

All of the Hopi knew about the huge canyon north of their dwellings about one hundred miles. It could be reached in just a week or two. The problem was that the canyon was huge, very deep, and it was hard to find anything there.

At that time in the early 1850s the Canyon was unexplored by the white man. I would be searching a totally unknown area.

My desire kept building to search for this lost underground city. I felt a pull drawing me there.

Chepi wanted to come with me and convinced me it would be useful to have a companion and an Indian who spoke the local languages and who would be able to converse with other Indians we met.

Fortunately, Hopis were the one tribe familiar with the Canyon and the elders gave Chepi and me more information to reach it safely and to climb down into it.

They suggested we go to the northeast to enter the canyon and build strong rafts to go down the fast river to discover what was there.

I already had a hatchet and a saw from my travels and we were certainly going to need them on the trip.

We took off on a sunny day in April with my two pack horses and Chepi riding another wild one which had been broken.

Heading north the trails were light. This was all Indian Territory and there were no western settlers.

The Grand Canyon

It took us several weeks to reach our goal which was the Colorado River north of the canyons.

We had met other Indians along the way but fortunately they were all peaceful and my being with a Hopi woman relaxed them a lot.

Chepi and I became very close. She was a good cook and good advisor to me on my plans and thinking.

We kept each other warm at night and became lovers too. It was one of the happiest times of my early life.

The river was still in a minor canyon and we had to navigate a foot trail to get down there. We went down a steep ancient trail which the Indians and local animals must have used for generations.

The area we descended to had a lot of trees since the area was pretty open and the canyon walls were a half mile wide at that location. The canyons depth was also only a hundred feet. Not really a canyon at all there.

Local Indians told us that the river was pretty rough further down and we were told we should not try to go down the river area since we would be killed.

I decided to build a boat to navigate the river.

We started building the next morning and some local Indians helped us. The boat was based on a design I knew from Wales which fishermen used to go out and fish on the sea.

It was flat bottomed and I hadn't built a boat before so I was guessing. I also put in lots of wooden ribs and spars to allow it to take lots of jolts and crashes on the rocks.

To keep from holing on the rocks we actually built a dual hull. The boat was only fifteen feet long, but had lots of room for the both of us and our supplies.

We had also craved lots of paddles and had some big sticks to push the boat against the rocks as needed.

It took us a month to build it even with lots of help, but I wanted to be sure that Chepi and I would be safe on the river.

We also wove some strong ropes from plants in the valley. There were various ropes which I wanted strong to hold the boat to locations in the river.

We asked the Indians if anyone had ever tried going down the river before.

They said there was a legend that old Spanish explorers had tried it but were never heard from again. Many attempts had been made to explore the canyon but most never returned.

Those who did return were scared for life and didn't say much except that Gods lived in the canyon.

*****

Chepi and I set off on a beautiful morning in early June in our homemade boat.

The river was not going too fast where we put in so we started enjoying our ride as the canyon walls came together and it got deeper.

The walls got steeper and steeper as the canyon became more impressive and narrower. Soon the water started moving faster and we had to use our paddles to avoid rocks and keep heading in the right direction.

After a couple of hours traveling the river I saw a sandy beach where we stopped for a break.

The temperature had risen to about ninety degrees Fahrenheit which was warm enough to keep us from getting cold from the cold river water splashing on us.

We had stopped next to a side canyon which I wanted to explore. We ate some food then hiked up the side canyon which was dry at the time although we could see signs of water being there often.

There were several caves and when we reached them we found old Indian village ruins-probably from that ancient culture the Anastasi.

After a couple of hours of sightseeing we headed back down the canyon towards our boat.

I could tell that we were going to see many side canyons and they question was which one should we go up to find the ancient civilization in my dreams.

That night we camped at another bend in the river where there was a good sized beach.

I dreamed again of the canyon and the journey up to the cave where the ancient masters lived.

Looked for markers in my dream that night so that if I saw the canyon again I would recognize it.

We travelled more days down the river and our supplies were running low. Saw an island where a stream was coming into the river and we stopped to hunt. I got my bow, Chepi got hers and we both looked for game.

We found some small game and saw tracks that a few Deer also lived in that area. After hunting for a few hours we got a couple of rabbits and tracked the deer up the side canyon with the stream.

I shot a small buck that was going up the stream and we skinned and dressed it out back on the island.

We decided to stay there for a few days to cut and cure the meat over a fire.

Chepi had a lot of skills doing this and I just helped while she pointed out the best places to cut the deer meat up.

She also built a basic smoker to smoke the meat to dry and preserve it,

We felt good about this new food and thought that if we were careful it would sustain us for another month or so.

My dreams kept up each night with the details of the canyon and the cave entrance getting clearer and clearer.

We came to a part of the canyon my intuition was telling me was dangerous and we needed something to slow us down in some big rapids.

Chepi knew me well enough by now to value my intuition so she didn't argue with me stopping.

I had some extra wood in the boat and decided to make a drag anchor behind the boat. I had seen some ships in the Indian

Ocean use drag anchors at night many years ago to slow the motion of the boat in drifting current.

The principle was to have a line attached to the stern of the boat. It was supposed to be weighted down so it dragged on the bottom providing friction but to not catch hold of the bottom. This weighting was often done with chains.

We didn't have chains so I looked for some thin rocks which would weight the rope but not catch on anything.

The resulting thick rope was fifteen feet long from the stern of the boat and about fifty pounds of long thin rocks to weight it down.

We got back onto the river and after half an hour saw that my intuition had been right again.

The canyon narrowed and the water became a lot faster.

I made sure the drag anchor was well tied and threw it out the stern.

It did exactly as planned. It slowed the boat down so we could control it while keeping us stable in the rushing current.

We rode through the canyon like a stable leaf on a pond with lots of waves. We were actually having fun riding the rapids in our stable boat.

That evening we pulled out on a sandbar again and had a nice fire to heat up some food and make soup.

I felt that we were getting closer to our destination and told Chepi. She was an adventurer like me and looked forward to new experiences.

The next day we came to an area which was pretty flat so the river slowed down a lot into kind of a small lake.

In the middle of this area was a side canyon to the left which the lake continued into.

I spied a rock formation in the canyon which told me this was the right place.

We paddled into the canyon for another mile before the lake stopped.

Then we beached the boat and tied supplies onto our backs for the rest of the journey.

The canyon narrowed and became a trail between some close canyon walls. We followed the trail for five miles until we came to a little open area with some trees and brush surrounded by canyon walls.

The City of Arakesh

Going up the wall were carved steps to a large cave opening. After eating some food and taking a break we started up the stairs.

We walked up to the steps and into the cave. The cave looked pretty old and had lots of stalactites and stalagmites.

I couldn't see the end of the cave so we started walking into it. Strangely, there was a cold blue light coming out of the rocks so it didn't get too dark.

We kept walking on the path and finally came to a door. The door was unusual because it was made of metal. In that era almost all doors were still made of wood.

It also had a wheel in the middle. I could see by the linkages connected to the wheel that they held the door closed.

Trying the wheel, it finally started to spin counterclockwise. When it stopped spinning I pulled on the door and it slowly opened. Very strange to find this in cave.

When it opened there was a long tunnel behind it which disappeared off into the distance. How could there be a tunnel like this way out in a cave in the wilderness?

We walked carefully into the tunnel which had some type of lights which didn't burn set into the walls to keep it lighted.

After walking for about ten minutes we came to a chamber with a door split in the middle vertically.

There was some type of control next to it. When I pressed the button, the doors split, each side going left or right. There was a little room on the other side. I'd never seen anything like it.

Remember this was before elevators had been invented in the western world.

We were already committed to this strange journey so we entered the little room. The doors then closed which scared us a little. Then the room started moving down. We could feel it moving. What an unusual experience.

The little room we were in continued going down for a couple of minutes. We didn't have any idea where we were going.

Finally, the doors opened again and we had descended into a very large space. We got out of the small room into a park and looked around at our surroundings. It was some type of cave that looked like it was miles across. The ceiling was so high that there seemed to be clouds near the top.

We were in some type of park full of trees, grass, and flowers.

We were also greeted by some older people dress in strange clothes.

One older man spoke English to us and said "Welcome to the city of Arakesh. My name is Melitor. I and these other people are elders here to welcome you."

I replied in a still wondering state "This is incredible. I don't understand how you could build something like this out in the wilderness and deep under the Grand Canyon. But thanks for your welcome."

Melitor smiled and replied "Here-follow me to sit down. Let's go over to these stone and wooden seats in the park where you can relax and we can talk more." Leading us to the area where we could all sit in a nice area of the park.

This side area of the park was surrounded by trees and with flowers all over near the chairs. It was obviously a meeting area set off from the rest of the park.

As we sat down he continued "We have been here many thousands of years, and have science and technology well in advance of anything on the surface of your world. Did any of the Indians tell you about how their ancestors came from here?"

"Yes" I said. "My friend Chepi's tribe are called the Hopi and claim they came from here thousands of years ago. It was an old legend and none of us really believed it."

Melitor said "Chepi I would like to learn the details of your Hopi legends in the future but let's talk now about what you can both do while you are here."

"Thank You" I said "I felt drawn here but didn't know why."

Melitor added "Yes—you were drawn here because our Spiritual Masters felt your presence in back in Tibet and thought we would both benefit by meeting each other. They have been directing you for a long time."

"You see our purpose is to protect the world above, and we need friends there who can help us accomplish our goals to help with the rise of civilization again on the Earth. This is why we stay secret. We don't want the people above to know we are guiding the world. You Trevor could be a big help with our efforts."

I said "Wow, that is quite a mission. I would of course like to know a lot more before I agree to do all this."

Melitor nodded his head and said "Yes of course-You have much to learn here as does your woman Chepi."

******

So we were taken to a housing area in a twenty story building. This building also had one of those vertical moving boxes which we learned were called "Lifts" in English. This made it much easier to get to the top of the building where Chepi and I were assigned a nice flat with several rooms including a bathroom with a miraculous ability.

It had a toilet seat with water underneath. When you sat and did your duty, there was a flush mechanism which flushed everything down pipes. Wow. We also had indoor plumbing too for hot and cold water.

I had heard that some of the very wealthy landowners and royalty had something like this. But had never seen anything as sophisticated as what was in our flat.

We were also assigned a guide to answer our questions and guide us around the city. Her name was Tilvi and she was a young but very energetic woman.

First, she told us how to work the bathroom, and when we were cleaned up and rested she invited us to the dining facility outside in a nearby building.

Inside the dining area was a line where everyone took plates on trays to get the food from cooks.

I'd seen something similar to this mass cooking in the British Army, but the food was much better here.

Tilvi took us on a tour of the city after dinner and we saw many large tall buildings and parks. Some of the buildings were almost a mile high.

This place was more advanced than anything I had ever heard of or seen. I was also told there were other underground cities accessible through long tunnels.

We went home to our flat and slept in wonder about where we were and what we had seen.

*****

Chepi and I were taken to another building the next day to meet with some Spiritual Masters. We shook hands and sat cross legged on rugs on the floor in a circle.

The head master introduced himself as "Levindo" and started to talk to us again in English "Welcome young Trevor and Chepi. We want to learn about your backgrounds. Trevor please tell us your history and don't spare any details."

So I told him all about being raised in Wales, joining the army, my travels, my intuition, the skills I'd learned in Tibet, various fights in different places, and everything I could think of. It took a couple of hours.

Chepi also talked of her life with the Hopis but of course didn't have the stories I did.

Levindo thanked us for our stories and then got into his main subject of how to help the world above.

"The surface world is still recovering from a tragic worldwide flood thousands of years ago. We see our job as guiding civilization strategically to make the right decisions to grow and evolve, without interfering in their cultures."

"We need a few well trained individuals who will live on the surface and get involved in large events to help change the course of history. We believe that you Trevor are one of those people."

I thought about this and said "So you must have had people out in the world before."

"Yes over many thousands of years. We only have a few people connected with us on the surface at any one time. The man who founded the Tibetan school you attended was one of those." Levindo continued.

Surprised I added "So you must have a lot of the Spiritual knowledge being taught to the world?"

"Yes—one of our masters wrote the Yoga Sutras of Patanjali several thousand years ago. We have been watching you using our intuitive skills over the years which is why we invited you here." said Levindo.

I finally had a mental pause. Now I understood why so many strange things had happened to me.

Now it made sense why I had so many teachers who were helping me to learn both fighting and spiritual siddhis and abilities.

Now I could see the pattern which had drawn me across most of the world to end up hear in the city of Arakesh.

Levindo was watching me and I knew he saw that I was now realizing how they had been directing his life for many years.

Trevor said "So you have been directing my life for many years and I'm here now. What do you want me to do from here?"

Levindo said "This is a choice to be one of our representatives to the world. You can leave if you are not interested. You need to make this decision now."

I thought about it and realized that what the Arakesh masters wanted me to do was in line with my life… to do good and help people. So I answered "Yes—what you want me to do is in line with my beliefs so I would love to be your representative to the surface world."

Levindo and the others nodded and said "This is good. We had hoped you would say yes. Now you will start a period of training which will last one year."

"We will teach you our science and technology. In other words the science and practical aspects of how things are built to support civilization and why. Your learning will be fast since we have speed learning technology."

I interrupted "So people like Leonardo Da Vinci might have been students of yours?"

Levindo smiled and said "Yes—he was, very brilliant but he did have our training and he gave technological ideas to the world— but many years ahead. As well as many great art works."

Levindo ended the meeting and we ate lunch there together. I had a chance to meet the other masters.

He told us that our training would start the next day. Chepi would learn too since they thought as did I that we would be spending much of our lives together.

The Psychic Soldier Series-Book 2-A Soldier is Born

Back To School

The next morning our guide took us to a Classical Greek type building with big columns. We were told that this was the city's main library and learning center.

Inside we were taken down a corridor to a good size room filled with beds and lots of electronic equipment, and a classroom area with a blackboard.

The man who would be our main teacher introduced himself "Hello Trevor and Chepi. It is a pleasure to meet you. My name is Master Chalabra. I will be your main instructor."

The Master continued "Your instruction will be of several types. First you will learn from machines which will plant the knowledge in your brain. Then you will have classes to help you learn to access and use your knowledge. Lastly there will be a separate spiritual class both of you will attend with other masters to work with each of you at your own levels."

"Your classes will be from basic elementary education all the way through advanced degrees and technology which will not appear on your world for hundreds of years."

I was really wowed by this and not having much formal education was looking forward to it.

Master Chalabra added "What you will learn in one year with our advanced training techniques will be equivalent to going to school for thirty years of regular time."

So we began our training being asked about form schooling we had previously. I had learned to read and write from my mother and had never been to school. Chepi had never attended any type of school except stories she learned from her elders.

The Psychic Soldier Series-Book 2-A Soldier is Born

Our teacher nodded and set the machines to start from early childhood education.

He said that each session of one hour would be equivalent to several months of normal schooling.

Then he had us lie down on couches near each other and put a light helmet over each of our heads.

The helmet made noises as it energized then we felt light electrical impulses entering our brains. It was a very pleasant experience and we dozed through it.

When we woke up and took off the helmets we felt refreshed.

Then the classroom session started. In the classroom we were asked to take tests and demonstrate what we had learned to the teacher.

This included writing simple sentences and doing arithmetic on the board using chalk.

The idea was for us to enable the knowledge and skills we had acquired in deep learning.

School lasted about five hours per day then it was time for lunch.

I asked Chepi how she like the schooling over lunch. She smiled and said "I never had an education and I'm so grateful for everything I'm learning. It is one of the best experiences of my life."

We toured the city more after lunch and made love back in our flat.

The next day was the same process in accelerated education, but I also had a Spiritual class afterwards.

I was taken to another building by my guide Tilvi. The Spiritual Building was a pyramid with multiple chambers inside.

The one I was led to had a nice rug with cushions the floor on top. I met Melitor there. It was surprising to see him. He said hello and that he occasionally taught spiritual classes and I was to be one of his special students.

We both sat cross legged on cushions facing each other and were the only two in the room.

Melitor said "There are many things you have learned spiritually, especially at the school in the Himalayas.

What I need to do is figure out what else is appropriate for me to teach you now. Other additional abilities will come to you with time.

I understand you have already learned to follow your intuition and can become invisible. That you were also taught longevity practices."

"Yes" I replied "These abilities have served me well travelling to many places as I have. Have done my best to practice everything I've learned."

He said "Well one thing you need is more practice on is Longevity. You will need to live many hundreds of years to accomplish our mission on the surface. So we will concentrate on practicing the techniques you learned to make sure they keep your body stable and alive for a long time."

So during these spiritual classes several times per week we practiced meditational techniques and longevity visualizations. I started to feel healthier and more stable over a period of weeks.

Melitor told me that the techniques were working and they would extend my healthy longevity for many decades-but I needed to continue to practice them on my own.

After six months of training both Chepi and I had progressed to the level of what we would today called advanced degrees in multiple disciplines.

We were learning about mathematics, science, technology, true world history, and languages. Our instruction also included military tactics, political science, and social dynamics.

In the classroom sessions we did practical science labs, solved math problems, and practiced languages with Chalabra who knew many languages.

*****

Our year was up and we had gone through an education worth the equivalent of multiple graduate degrees at a large university in the surface world.

We hadn't realized how ignorant we were, and could now see the trends of industrial and technology growth in our world. Our knowledge also raised many additional questions like where the civilization in Arakesh came from originally.

But it was time to leave. We would have to get our questions answered in the future.

Melitor and the other Masters we knew gave us a going away party. At the party Melitor gave us this going away speech:

"Trevor and Chepi we are so happy you decided to stay with us this last year. We have done our best to teach you useful knowledge as you make your way in the world.

The Psychic Soldier Series-Book 2-A Soldier is Born

Here is a special communicator to contact us when you need advice or help. It is in the shape of a copper medallion to wear. It is not made of precious metals so there is less chance of it being stolen. But it does link to a stealth satellite we have around the Earth to reach us wherever you are."

I remembered the one that Minister Valdasian had around his neck in Peking, China. I remarked "That looks like the medallion that one of my mentors Minister Valdasian work in Peking."

Melitor smiled and said "Yes-He is one of our representatives monitoring the Chinese Empire. He was one who alerted us to your existence. Now please take these medallions with our blessings."

What was unsaid was that I had received the longevity training and Chepi had not. We would have a happy life together but it would be a lot shorter that my life going forward.

After lots of hugs and well wishes we took our goodbyes.

*****

Our guide Tilpi led us to an easier exit from the hidden city than going back to our boat and down the Grand Canyon the rest of the way.

The exit was on the side of the canyon up on the plateau. We also had the supplies we had packed a couple of horses Tilpi's people gave us.

The Psychic Soldier Series-Book 2-A Soldier is Born

Back with the Hopis

Chepi had an idea where we were so she headed us south. In a couple of weeks we were back in the Hopi community she had been raised in.

We told the elders about our travels and they were awed, giving us both great respect in the community.

Chepi asked me to stay with her and raise children together which we did.

I helped wrangle horses and made occasional trips to Santa Fe to trade for the tribe.

We spent Many years together and raised a family on the Hopi reservation.

Chepi knew that I would outlive her and remain young, so we lived the life we had as best we could.

I knew that I would have more adventures in the future and this was just the beginning of my life and my adventures.

But for now, it was a nice life and I intended to enjoy it.

The End of The Psychic Warrior Series Book 2

If you have any comments or would like more psychic warrior
adventures please send your comments to:

Marty@personal-longevity.com